Thelma Smallwood GARDNER

PROPERTY OF

NEKL

Y0-BQN-294

The Ten Gifts

BOOKS BY
ELIZABETH GOUDGE

ISLAND MAGIC

A CITY OF BELLS

A PEDLAR'S PACK

TOWERS IN THE MIST

THE MIDDLE WINDOW

THE SISTER OF THE ANGELS

THE BIRD IN THE TREE

SMOKY HOUSE

THE GOLDEN SKYLARK

THE WELL OF THE STAR

THE HEART OF THE FAMILY

THE BLUE HILLS

THE CASTLE ON THE HILL

GREEN DOLPHIN STREET

THE ELIZABETH GOUDGE READER

THE LITTLE WHITE HOUSE

SONGS AND VERSES

PILGRIM'S INN

GENTIAN HILL

THE REWARD OF FAITH

GOD SO LOVED THE WORLD

THE VALLEY OF SONG

THE ROSEMARY TREE

THE WHITE WITCH

MY GOD AND MY ALL

THE DEAN'S WATCH

THE SCENT OF WATER

A BOOK OF COMFORT

A DIARY OF PRAYER

A CHRISTMAS BOOK

A BOOK OF PEACE

THE TEN GIFTS

The Ten Gifts

ELIZABETH GOUDGE

SELECTED BY MARY BALDWIN

COWARD-McCANN, Inc.
NEW YORK

JOHNSON COUNTY LIBRARY
SHAWNEE MISSION, KANSAS

Copyright © 1934, 1939, 1940, 1942, 1944, 1948, 1949, 1950, 1953, 1956, 1958, 1960, 1963, 1969 by Elizabeth Goudge

FIRST AMERICAN EDITION 1969

All rights reserved. This book, or parts thereof, may not be reproduced in any form without permission in writing from the Publisher.

Library of Congress Catalog
Card Number: 73-99287

PRINTED IN THE UNITED STATES OF AMERICA

Contents

C.4

TRUTH

COURAGE

FOREWORD

The choice of selections for this anthology has been a mixture of delight and regret. Delight, because the reading and rereading of Elizabeth Goudge's stories always reveals something fresh and stimulating. Regret, because from the abundance of material so much has had to be left out.

Elizabeth Goudge is one of those rare writers who recognizes that the whole man is made up of body, mind and spirit, and her own shining spirit is reflected throughout her books. She shows the light and dark sides of life vividly, realistically, yet lifts the edge of the darkness and one is aware that the light will prevail.

In these times of wars and violence and falling moral values she helps to restore the balance, and the fact that so many readers turn to her, and in doing so take away some of the fruits of her spirit, augurs well for the future.

Mary Baldwin

INTRODUCTION

An anthology such as this one is the work of two people, the one who makes the anthology and the one from whose works it is made. The selections show the anthologist's own attitude and response to life and to our living of it. And so this book is as much Mary Baldwin's as mine, and I am most grateful to her for the skillful making of it. She believes that our true wealth in life is our spiritual wealth, the gifts of the Spirit that are the gifts of God alone. St. Paul speaks of "the unsearchable riches of Christ," since only in Christ the perfect human being are all the gifts of the Spirit supremely discovered. But we imperfect men and women can, according to our capacity and willingness, receive a few of them. Our capacity is not great, since only the single-minded are not cluttered up with rubbish, and our willingness uncertain, since God never gives gifts without demanding that we shall use them, which can be painful, but nevertheless how we do love and reverence them when we see them shining from use in our friends. Love. Wonder. Beauty. Delight. Compassion. Understanding. Faith. Tranquillity. Truth. Courage. These are ten jewels from the inexhaustible, unsearchable treasury of God. I have loved them in my friends and, as a storyteller, have delighted in giving one of them here and there to the imagined people in my books. But are the people in one's stories as much our own creation as we storytellers like to think they are? I think it would be truer to say that they are a mosaic of the real people the writer has known, and wherever a jewel turns up in the mosaic, it is a real jewel once worn, or worn still, by some real person as a gift of God.

And so we come back to the threefold thing, the giver, the recipient, and the gift itself, the eternal Trinity that runs through the whole of life.

ELIZABETH GOUDGE

LOVE

A BOY AND A MAID

IT was this reverence of his that set the minds of Father and
Mother Sprigg instantly at rest about Zachary and Stella. That
he loved the little girl and found her the delight of his life it
was plain to see, and she followed him about like his gleeful
shadow, yet the daily companionship bred no carelessness in him;
he treated her always as though someone had just that moment put
into his hands some treasure that could be sullied by a breath or
smashed by a hasty movement. Yet though they did not worry,
Father and Mother Sprigg marvelled a little at the companionship
between the two. They had only just come together yet they seemed
now not properly themselves when they were apart. Zachary, coming into the farm kitchen and not finding Stella there, would for a
moment or two look like a lost dog. Stella, if Zachary were late,
would drift round in a bewildered way, exactly like a small shadow
which had lost its substance. Yet when the one who was awaited
came they would have no exuberant greeting for each other; they
would just relax and be themselves again, a divided thing made
whole. There was something here that went deeper than the
normal affection of two young things for each other and puzzled
Father and Mother Sprigg.

It did not puzzle Dr. Crane, aware that he was in the presence of
Shakespeare's marriage of two minds, yet he observed this rare
thing with interest, never to his knowledge having met it before.
Shakespeare was right, it had nothing to do with the body, and
undoubtedly it was true in the sense of being a thing that could
not pass. As to the why of it, that was beyond him. A man might as
well ponder the "why" of the dawn and the spring. The element of
eternity in these things stood as a witness to something. Better
leave it at that. He did so, meanwhile perceiving with delight how
the various contrasts in the dispositions of these two locked one
into the other, built firmly upon the foundation of their unities.
Stella's fearlessness and Zachary's fear, her love of adventure and

his of security, her serenity and his anxiety, she with her externe's sensitiveness to the suffering of others and he with the interne's power of suffering unduly in his own mind and body. And both of them with their gift, perhaps quite natural in two whose vocation it seemed to be to shadow forth the timelessness of love, of apprehending and making contact with that which exists behind the appearance of things. And both of them, too, with the artist's love of beauty and the scholar's love of learning that are part of that gift.

THE ADOPTED SON

THE turmoil of packing over, and the two young men tactfully gone to bed early, Dr. Crane and Zachary sat for the last time talking in front of the study fire. The doctor had a few things that he wanted to say and he said them, though with small hope that they would penetrate the wretchedness of the boy beside him.

"You've done the right thing, Zachary, though as far as you can see it's not done you any good. Not much glory about it as far as you can see. You feel damnable. That's of no consequence—feelings don't matter. It's action that matters, and from fine action some sort of glory always breaks in the end; though God knows how long you may have to wait for it."

"What *is* glory?" growled Zachary suddenly.

"I can't explain. You'll know one day. But there's one thing which out of my doctor's experience both in war and peace I think I can explain, and that's how to deal with fear." Zachary started, and the doctor thanked God that he had captured his attention. "To begin with, don't fight it, accept it without shame, just as you would accept any other limitation you happen to be born with, a cast in the eye, or a lame foot. Willing acceptance is half the battle, as you've probably discovered before this. Be willing to be afraid, don't be afraid of your fear. As a doctor I can tell you that every man has within him a store of strength, both physical and spiritual, of which he is utterly unaware until the moment of crisis. You will not tap it until the moment of crisis, but you can be quite certain that when that moment comes it will not fail you. It's not easy to believe this, but you must do it. And there's another thing which you must do; learn to live with alien horrors and not let your nerves crack beneath the pressure of them." Again Zachary started, remembering his relief when he came to this house and realized that the fight to hold off that pressure was over at last. "Again, don't fight; if you fight you'll crack. You can't fight foul language, foul smells, sweat and dirt and all the rest of it, the only thing you can do is to live amongst it both with acceptance and withdrawal. That sounds paradoxical but it's perfectly possible. You're not befouled by another man's obscenities and brutalities, though you may feel you are, but only by your own, and if you have strangled your own then the door of escape is open for you and you can go through it to the fortress when you wish. There is a fortress, you know."

Zachary knew. The stones of the Chapel had cried it out, and later, through that extra sense that adversity had developed in him his mind had grasped the existence of that something behind. Yet what is the use of knowing a thing, he thought bitterly, when you are unable personally to experience the truth of it? Your knowledge is about as useful in the darkness as a lantern with no light in it.

"You can experience the reality of what you believe in only one way, by putting it to the test," said the doctor, interpreting his silence aright. "There is nothing at all that will light up the flame in your lantern except the wind of your going. Nothing else at all."

They were silent, and then Zachary said slowly, "I've said good-bye to Stella." He felt he wanted the doctor to know how he felt about Stella, yet it seemed unexplainable.

"She'll not forget you," said the doctor, as though no explanation were necessary.

"She's only a little girl," said Zachary, moving restlessly in his chair. "I can't expect . . ."

"A very unusual little girl," said the doctor, "of whom unusual things may be expected. She is not the child of Father and Mother Sprigg."

Zachary suddenly sat straight up in his chair, tense and eager. "Not the child of the Spriggs! Does she know that?"

"Yes, she knows."

"Why, sir, she never told me!"

"I imagine that loyalty to Mother Sprigg would have kept her from telling you. Mother Sprigg is possessive and likes it to be thought that Stella is really her child. Stella, with her intuition, would sense that. But I think it is right that you should know. You'll keep your mouth shut."

"Yes, sir."

Dr. Crane, thankful to give Zachary something to think about apart from his own misery, told all that he knew of Stella, and Zachary listened eagerly. "That explains her," he said. "I could not understand where she got it from—her wisdom—not like a child's."

"Father and Mother Sprigg have plenty of wisdom."

"Not that sort. Unearthly. As though she were a fairy's child."

"She's human all right." The doctor laughed, went to his desk and came back with a folded scrap of paper. "This was written inside Stella's mother's locket. I copied it out in the Greek in which it was written. Your Greek is equal to the strain, I think. And you know *The Banquet*."

Zachary took the scrap of paper and translated slowly. "'Love is the divinity who creates peace among men, and calm upon the sea, the windless silence of storms, repose and sleep in sadness. Love sings to all things which love and are, soothing the troubled minds of gods and men.'"

Zachary had read the words often and they had had little meaning for him, yet now in his extremity it seemed as though they had actually been written for him. For a sudden brief moment he was in that core of quiet that exists at the heart of every storm; the fortress. He folded the paper again.

"You can keep it," said the doctor. "And now we'd better go to bed."

16

INARTICULATE LOVE

"WHEN I had finished reading the story for the first time I was ashamed of my despair but I also had a new joy and a new sense of direction. I must use my hands more, I thought. I did not mean it literally, for I am stupid with my hands, I can't carve or paint and even the seams I sew are never straight. What I meant was that I must build something up for somebody, make something to put into the hands of another when I die. But what could I make, and for whom?

"I was wondering about this when the old spaniel began to thump his tail on the floor and then the door opened and Mr. Ambrose came in surrounded by the usual cloud of dogs. Mr. Ambrose is red-faced, awkward and inarticulate. How he comes to be the son of his charming and most articulate parents is a mystery. Yet no one has ever been contemptuous of Mr. Ambrose. His heart, they say, is in the right place. I like Mr. Ambrose immensely, and though he seldom speaks to me, and generally blushes furiously when I speak to him, I am somehow aware that he likes me. He came up to my chair, knocking into the furniture as he came, blushed purple, laid a small box on my knee and said, 'For you.'

"'For me?' I asked. 'A present, Mr. Ambrose?'"

"He nodded and whispered hoarsely, 'Saw it in the window. Thought you'd like it.'

"I took the lid off the little box and lifted the cotton wool inside. At my elbow Mr. Ambrose was breathing as heavily as though he had been running a race, and all the dogs were trembling and taut with eagerness about me. Mr. Ambrose is so united with his dogs that they share his every emotion. Under the cotton wool was something small and white and delicate. I picked it up and my breath caught in my throat so that I could not speak. It was a carved ivory coach, about the size of a hazel nut, and inside was Queen Mab. There are no words to describe the loveliness of that coach, like a sea shell, or the beauty of the little queen's face half-smiling beneath her tiny crown.

"I held it in the palm of my hand and it seemed to be all that there is. With a flash of knowledge I knew that Mr. Ambrose had in truth put into my hand all that there is, all he has. He does more than like me, I know now. For years he has more than liked me and I suppose deep inside me I have more than liked him. Abnormality may forbid the normal course of love between man and woman but it does not preclude the love, as normal people so often seem to think, it merely drives it underground to a great depth. This gift in my hand told me more about the inarticulate man beside me than if he had talked about himself for a week on end. That he should have noticed this tiny thing in a shop window, should have liked it, told me what he was. That he should have known that I would like it, told me how much he knew about me. I could have wept only what I was feeling strangled tears. But the increasing heaviness of Mr. Ambrose's breathing, the rising anxiety of the dogs, told me that I had to do something simple that Mr. Ambrose would understand. I held the little coach against my cheek and then I got up and took Mr. Ambrose's hand and laughed for joy. And it really was joy though a moment before I could have wept. I was so glad that he had found the way to tell me, even if he himself was largely unaware of what he had told me, and I was so happy for us both that we had this hidden love. At the sound of my laughter his face was wreathed in smiles and all the dogs relaxed into tail-wagging relief. Then the old butler came in with the tea-tray and Mr. Ambrose and I had tea together and talked about my collection of little things.

"When he had gone and I was alone again I sat and looked at Queen Mab and I saw that she had a child's face, and suddenly I knew what I was going to make, a home for the child. Not just the little carved ivory child but for the child whom this toy represents and who will one day come into my life. I cannot even imagine yet who she will be but I feel sure she will come. I have often wondered who will live in The Laurels when I die. My next of kin is my sister but a house like The Laurels, a place like Appleshaw, would neither of them mean anything to her. If The Laurels went to her she would only sell it. But now I see what to do. This child, my child, will come and she will have The Laurels and all I possess. I will set to work to make the garden as lovely as I can. I will plant flowering shrubs and rose trees and make a waterlily pool, and find a cupid or a dolphin boy to watch over it till she comes. And I will take great care of the house for her. She will love my little things. It is for her of course that I have been collecting them. I didn't know that until now. I feel one with her, as though we were the same woman. She will find great happiness in all that I have prepared for her, and, in her, so shall I. 'They that sow in tears shall reap in joy.' Perhaps she will even reap my faith, as I believe I have reaped that of the old man.''

CINDERELLA AND HER DOLL

THEY looked at the path and the safety of it tingled in the soles of their feet. Upon the other side of the stile the air was very blue and there was laughter there. Suddenly feeling brave they got through the stile and ran through the green sea, and its terror curled away back from the path like the terror of the sea when the Israelites marched through it singing, and they came in safety to the cave in the rock.

Here they crouched down again, on the floor of the cave, for though they were no longer afraid their awe was great. "That's a door," whispered Meriful, for he had seen doors, though never a door as big as this one. It was not latched, and presently they crept forward and applied their eyes to the crack. Cortez, upon that peak in Darien, had felt no greater thrill. They leaned against the door and slowly it creaked open a few inches, and a few inches more. They stopped, all in delicious wonder and confusion, then leaned again, and laughed, and then they went through. Hand in hand they stood just within the door and gazed in amazement at this vast cavern in the mountain to which the small cave had admitted them.

It seemed to them so vast but it was in reality a small

grey-arched Norman church, dim and cool and musty-smelling. The sun shone through the opaque green glass in the small windows as through water, and the green light lay gently on the worn flagstones, the old rood screen and oak benches. The church was full of shadows and hidden among them were old tombs and the escutcheons of dead knights. There was a stone pulpit and an altar with a silver cross upon it, for Parson Hawthyn was a Laudian and refused to take away the cross or any of the church ornaments, retaining the full ritual of the Church of England and wearing his surplice let Robert say what he would. The villagers did not mind what he did for he was beloved, and they were accustomed to his ways.

It was a long time before the children dared the shadows but presently, still feeling safety in the soles of their feet and aware of peace in the green light and laughter in the floating motes of golden dust, they essayed them. They found the lady first, lying on her tomb in her best gown with a ruff round her neck, her head on a cushion and her feet resting against a strange little horse with a thorn sticking out of his forehead. To begin with they thought the tomb was a rock and so they were not frightened. It was only when they stood on tiptoe and felt the strange shapes with their hands that they realized that a lady and a tiny horse had been turned into stone by some chovihan. But still they were not frightened, for the magic felt good to them and they supposed the act to have been beneficent. They made their way from one wonder to the other, bobbing up and down among the benches and tombs, flitting from the green sea light to the shadows again like bright butterflies in their gay rags. They lost all sense of time and they did not know that they were hungry.

It was Cinderella who all by herself discovered Madona. Parson Hawthyn had among other eccentricities a gift for carving wooden figures and making them gay with paint and gilding, and he had set a few here and there about the church. A couple of little cherubs sat upon a window-sill and looked down upon the font, and in various nooks and crannies perched birds: robins, chaffinches and kingfishers with hoods of blue. Cinderella did not see the cherubs, for she did not look so high, and the birds she took to be real birds, but what she did discover was Madona with a baby in her arms, almost hidden in a niche in the wall. She knew it was Madona, even though Madona's cloak was brown and this cloak was blue, because of the smile upon her face. Madona smiled just like that when some mother brought a new baby and laid it on her lap. And that was the way she smiled when Cinderella sat upon her knee. And that was the way Cinderella herself would smile if she could have that baby. She had wept for the loss of her bit of stick, but what was a bit of stick, even mossy and with two arms to it, to a baby like this, a real baby with a golden head and pink feet and a white diklo tied round its middle?

Scarcely breathing, her eyes like stars and her cheeks crimson, she stretched her hands to the niche and touched the baby. She had meant only to touch but as soon as her fingers felt the wood she could feel the baby in her arms. She, who had never had a toy, knew suddenly, in a great gust of delight, the full passion of a little girl's love for a real doll. She must have it. Her fingers closed upon it. And then she felt an agony of apprehension. Was it fixed on to Madona's knees, or would it lift off? Madona's hands were curved beneath the baby, as though offering it to Cinderella, but, when it came to the point, would they let go? Cinderella gave a pull, but Madona's hands held tight, for though the two little figures were separate the paint had not been quite dry when Parson Hawthyn had laid the baby on his mother's lap. Cinderella began to sob with apprehension. Then she pulled again and Madona suddenly let go.

She ran to the lady's tomb and squatted down beside it to nurse her baby. He was about twelve inches long and the golden head fitted into the crook of her elbow as though it had always been there. She pulled up a fold of her ragged blue skirt and wrapped it round him as a cloak. She began to try and sing the song that Madona had sung to her when she was a baby, her tiny piping voice clear and true as a wren's. It was the lullaby that all gypsy mothers sang to their children, and they said it was the song Mary had sung to her Baby when they lived in Egypt. Meriful, hearing her singing, began to whistle the tune as he sat up above her astride the tomb, his orange tawny jerkin bright as a robin's breast in a green gold finger of sun, whacking up the little horse and riding to the fair.

Dinki was too busy to sing, for he was running up and down the pulpit steps, but the patter of his bare feet sounded like the song of the rain on the leaves accompanying the whistling and piping of the robin and wren. The music was so small that it made scarcely more sound than the unheard laughter that had come with the children out of the wood.

PARSON HAWTHYN'S CHRISTMAS SERMON

"IT's Christmas Day, Will!" she cried. "It's Christmas and the bells are ringing!"

Well wrapped up against the cold, and carrying posies of herbs to counteract the aroma of any neighbours in church who might wash less frequently than they did themselves, the Haslewood family walked through the beechwood, and behind them at a respectful distance came Biddy and the two little maids, also carrying posies. Robert walked in sombre silence and Margaret walked beside him, her hand in his arm. She felt more cheerful now, for when they had come out of the house Robert had very deliberately turned his back upon Froniga, who was now walking behind with the children, and offered his arm to his wife. He had even smiled at her, a wintry sort of smile, but one intended for her alone. She held his arm tightly, feeling that she was supporting and helping him. Now and then she fancied that he pressed her hand against his side. If it was only fancy it still made her happy.

There was joy in Froniga's heart as she came behind with Jenny and Will, for through the whole of her sensitive being she was aware of blessedness. It was the same sort of awareness that came to her sometimes on a winter's night in the middle of a storm. She would go to her window, draw back the curtains and see that the driving clouds had parted as though a hand had drawn them aside like a curtain, and in a pool of tranquil sky she would see a few stars gleaming. The storm was not over, it would rage on until it had blown itself out, but the depth of mercy beyond had shown itself. That pool of sky held all the springtimes of the world. And so it was with the storms that men in their wickedness chose to let loose on the world. They must spend themselves. But now and then, through them and in spite of them, mercy shone, imposing some pattern upon the flux of things. Froniga knew now, as the children had known for some while, that this was to be a happy Christmas.

Jenny and Will upon either side of her went along as though they had wings upon their feet. Unable to walk fast because of their parents' slow progress, their exuberance expressed itself in sudden upward leaps or dartings sideways, like birds in spring. The snow was thinly spread, crisp and sparkling, and the pattern of their small feet made upon it only a delicate tracery. In the wood the shadows were violet and azure about the trunks of the trees, and far overhead the frosted branches made a silver filigree against the brilliant blue of the sky. The music of the bells, upon which no one had made any comment, seemed now to be ringing through the aisles of the wood and raining down upon them from the sky. Froniga realized with amusement that this year they were being rung for a longer period than usual, and with greater vigour and beauty.

When they reached the common they saw other family groups making their way to the church. From every cottage and farm they were coming out in their gay best clothes, that were kept for most of the year in presses and chests and brought out only on fair days and festivals. The gowns of blue and apricot, the red and green cloaks, made each family look like a flower-garden in bloom upon the sparkling snow. Froniga had never seen so many churchgoers. Never mind what brings them, she thought, curiosity or anger, pride or pity, the pattern will be imposed on us all when we are there.

With the bells ringing out over their heads they passed the ruins of the little parsonage, and Robert forced himself to turn his head and look at them steadily. Then they went on through the church-yard, where the snow had hidden the remains of yesterday's bonfire. Robert found himself oddly thankful for that. The ashes of Parson Hawthyn's little figures, and the blackened cross, would have made him even more wretched than the sight of the parsonage, for that destruction he had intended and the other he had not. Yet he was ashamed of his softness that could still desire so passionately the esteem and love of those about him, and hate to hurt their feelings. Did that great man of God, Colonel Cromwell, consider feelings? No! Whenever idolatry confronted him he was an avenging sword in the hand of the Lord. Would Colonel Cromwell's heart have failed within him at the thought of standing up before a hostile congregation, whose papistical priest he had driven away, and proclaiming the word of the Lord in his stead? No. His voice would have been as a brazen trumpet, and his words winged fire. Removing his hat as he came to the porch, Robert closed his eyes and prayed for strength.

He opened them and found himself looking into the bright eyes of Parson Hawthyn, and thought with a sense of shock and confusion that no one in the world had such piercing, farseeing blue eyes, excepting only Colonel Cromwell himself. He paused, clearing his throat, trying to find the courage to tell the old man he was not to take the service today, and found that he was trembling. "A happy Christmas to you, sir," said Parson Hawthyn loudly and cheerfully, before he could speak, "And to you, madam, and to you, mistress, and to Jenny and Will. Peace to you all." His voice dropped. "Peace to you, Robert. The peace of God." His voice rose again, ringing out cheerfully. "A happy Christmas to you, Sam Tidmarsh. And to you, Mistress Wilkins. A happy Christmas to you all."

There was such a press of people behind them that Robert was forced to move forward. Stumbling a little, his head aching from the clanging of the bells, he let Margaret lead him to their accustomed seat and sat down, covering his face with his hat.

When at the conclusion of his prayer he removed his hat he found that Jenny was upon his other side. She looked up at him and smiled, but it was a careful smile with a pitying tenderness in it, the kind of smile she might have given an afflicted stranger she was passing in the street, and it hurt him unbearably, when he remembered the hopes he had placed upon this Christmas. He looked across his wife to Will upon her other side, and then to Froniga. Margaret and Froniga were looking at him with anxiety, and when he smiled at them their answering smiles were those of

24

intense relief. Why? He looked round the church and saw why. The cross, tarnished and battered but intact, was back upon the altar. The flowers that he had flung on the ground had been rearranged in their pots upon either side of it. Fresh greenery and holly, exquisitely arranged, decorated the pulpit and the screen and the tomb of his grandmother. Except for the loss of the little figures everything was almost as it had been, and in his bewildered state he had noticed nothing when he had come in. It was his absence of protest that was causing such relief to his family. He felt not anger, but sorrow. Who had done this to him? Who had rendered null and void all he had tried to do for the Lord? Parson Hawthyn had himself perhaps found the cross and put it back, but the beauty of the green garlands was beyond the old man's powers. He looked at Froniga, who smiled and bent her head. The bells stopped and behind him the viols and flutes in the gallery, whose music he had forbidden, led the congregation triumphantly into the first hymn. As the surge of singing rose about him, louder and more triumphant than he had ever heard it on Christmas Day, Robert gave up the struggle. He was defeated. Physical weakness and family love had him in chains.

Yet as the service went on he was aware of freedom. He felt curiously untrammelled, as though he looked down upon his body from above it, as though he were dead and had left its weakness and pain behind him. He was scarcely aware of the details of the familiar service going on around him, but he was intensely aware of the ascension of prayer and praise; and not from this place only, but from every diverse place in every diverse circumstance wherein upon this day men prayed and gave thanks. It lifted him free of the limitations of the body and then free of the limitations of the mind too. When it reaches the blue illimitable air, the fire from many divided hearths loses itself in the one sunshine. For the space of a couple of minutes Robert also lost himself.

With extraordinary gentleness, as though upon wings, he sank down again to awareness of his surroundings. He had been carried down on the words of a prayer. Parson Hawthyn's voice was always beautiful, but today it had a burning sincerity which made each word seem living as well as lovely.

"Bless, O gracious Father, Thine holy Catholic Church. Fill it with truth and grace. Where it is corrupt purge it; where it is in error direct it; where it is superstitious rectify it; where it is amiss reform it; where it is right strengthen and confirm it; where it is divided and rent asunder heal the breaches of it. O Thou holy one of Israel."

Robert had said a loud amen before he remembered that Archbishop Laud had written that prayer. Though he was once more imprisoned within his painful body and his narrow mind, he felt no more than a passing embarrassment. Whoever had written them, the words were good. Misguided men did occasionally escape into truth. He knew that now, for he had just done it himself.

The concourse of viols and flutes in the gallery played the air of another hymn. They sounded like thrushes in spring. Then the congregation got to its feet and sang with such full-throated heartiness that the viols had to uplift their music to the utmost, like a stormcock who sings against the wind and rain. When the hymn was over Parson Hawthyn was seen to be in the pulpit.

The congregation was tingling with expectation. What would he say? This was the first Christmas of the war. A great battle had been fought and there would be more to come. The future was dark with suffering and disaster. Not only the church but the country was "divided and rent asunder". Even their own village had been rent with differences between squire and parson. And now the squire was in the congregation and the parson in the pulpit. What would the parson say?

"Good people," said Parson Hawthyn, "I am not going to speak to you today in my own words, because I believe that in times of conflict and emotion men often speak words that after they are sorry for. Therefore the sermon I shall preach to you will not be my own but that of another. Good people, eighteen years ago today, just a few weeks before I came to be the vicar of this parish, I was in St. Paul's Cathedral, and I heard Dean John Donne preach upon the mercy of God. I was able afterwards to write the sermon down but, alas, I cannot read it all to you because the book in which I wrote it has been accidentally destroyed. And so now I can only repeat to you that portion of it which I learned by heart and which my poor memory has retained. It will take but a few minutes, and will be the shortest sermon I have ever preached to you, but I bid you listen carefully, for in all the sorrow and conflict of our day there is one thing, and one thing only, which never fails us, and that is the mercy of God. And so, good people, 'we will speak of that which is older than our beginning, and shall overlive our end, the mercy of God. Nay, to say that mercy was first is but to post-date mercy; to prefer mercy but so is to diminish mercy. The names of first or last derogate from it, for first and last are but rags of time, and His mercy hath no relation to time, no limitation in time. It is not first or last, but eternal, everlasting. Let the devil make me so far desperate as to conceive a time when there was no mercy, and he hath made me so far an atheist as to conceive a time when there was no God. As long as there hath been love, and God is love, there hath been mercy. And mercy, in the practice and in the effect, began not at the helping of man when he was fallen and become miserable, but at the making of man, when man was nothing. . . . God . . . brought light out of darkness, not out of a lesser light. He can bring thy summer out of winter, though thou have no spring. Though in the ways of fortune, or misunderstanding, or conscience, thou have been benighted till now, wintered and frozen, cloudy and eclipsed, damp and benumbed, smothered and stupefied till now, now God comes to thee, not as in the dawning of the day, not as in the bud of the spring, but as the sun at noon, to banish all shadows; as the sheaves in harvest, to fill all penuries. All occasions invite His mercies, and all times are His seasons . . . God goes forward in His own ways, and proceeds as He began, in mercy. One of the most convenient hieroglyphics of God is a circle, and a circle is endless. Whom God loves He loves to the end; and not only to their own end, to their death, but to His end; and His end is, that He might love them still."

LUCILLA'S CONFESSION

"**I** WANT to tell you something that happened to me when I was young," she began abruptly and bravely. "I had not meant ever to tell anyone but this morning I changed my mind. Or rather Hilary changed it for me. He made me see that if I told it you would realize that I sympathize with you, and that I understand your feeling for one another. I do not think one has the right to give an opinion on any subject unless one has oneself experienced the emotion of it."

"May I smoke, Grandmother?" interrupted David politely but firmly. If Lucilla was going to tell them tales of her youth they would be here all morning, for there was no holding her when once she embarked upon the past.

"Of course, dear," said Lucilla, but she felt a little put out. When men smoked they became so somnolent. You could never tell if they were listening to a word you were saying. The interruption, too, had upset her. "Where was I?" she asked, a little plaintively.

". . . oneself experienced the emotion of it," prompted Nadine gently, and gave Lucilla a little comic glance of commiseration that was very warming. Nadine, unlike most other women of her type and generation, did not smoke. She was too fastidious. She didn't like the way lipstick came off on her cigarette.

"I was very young when I married," said Lucilla. "I was younger than you were, Nadine, when you married George. And I was not in love with my husband; he was a widower and much older than I and, poor dear, so plain. And I did not know when I married what marriage meant, either. Young girls never had things explained to them in those days. It was all a great shock to me. And then, you know, having been married before, there was nothing romantic about marriage to James, and though he meant to be kind he treated me in such a way that there was none for me either. I had five children much too quickly, and I am afraid I did not want

28

them at all. Later, when I was older, I loved all my children very
dearly, but when they were little I am afraid I did not think them
worth the bother and pain. I was so very young. Though I am a
naturally happy person I was very unhappy all through those early
years. I was quite dreadfully unhappy and I am afraid I almost
hated my good kind James."

She paused and her two listeners looked at her in astonishment.
Somehow they had both always imagined Lucilla's married life as
one of idyllic Victorian bliss. Now her short, difficult sentences
gave quite another picture.

"I was very ill when Stephen, my fifth child, was born," said
Lucilla, "and after that I rebelled. I told James that I would not
have any more children. He was very upset, poor James. He was an
ardent man, and he loved me. His mother had had thirteen
children and had given him very decided ideas about the duties of
a wife. He thought I was failing him very badly . . . I think,"
sighed Lucilla, "that if he hadn't gone on about his mother so
much my married life might have been happier."

Nadine was now definitely very interested. Her married life,
too, would have been very much happier if George had not gone on
so much about Lucilla. One of the odd things about men was that
though they always swore that women were the very devil yet they
always thought their mothers perfect . . . Lucilla, so George had
told her, had delighted in bearing six children to an adored
husband, Lucilla had been utterly contented with the home circle,
Lucilla had never flirted, Lucilla . . .

"Grandmother," asked Nadine wickedly, "did you ever flirt at
all?"

"Just a little, dear," confessed Lucilla modestly, "but not
enough for James to notice. You see, dear," she added with a
touch of pride, "I was very pretty when I was young."

"Grandmother," said Nadine, smiling, "this is getting most
exciting. I feel as though your life story was going to be a Victorian
melodrama. Surely, Grandmother, you didn't behave like the
heroine of East Lynne? I can't believe it of you."

"'Dead, and never called me mother'," quoted David delightedly.

His amusement hurt Lucilla and put her out again, and she stopped dead in her story. He was instantly penitent. "I'm sorry, Grandmother," he cried. "I'm sorry," and threw his cigarette into the fire to please her.

Nadine was sorry too. "Forgive us," she said. "It was because we don't believe it of you that we teased you. Please go on, Grandmother."

"I am afraid, my dears," said Lucilla slowly, "that you must believe it of me. I think a woman's history is very often like one of those old romances that you laugh at. Mine was, and so, Nadine," she added a little sharply, "is yours. You may laugh at them but they were truer to life than many of those psychological novels you young people read nowadays. We women don't sit half the day and night analysing our emotions but we do perpetually fall in love out of wedlock, and over and over again we have to fight out the same old battle between love and duty. Human emotions are very monotonous," sighed Lucilla. "Poor human nature doesn't get much change . . . Now where was I when you interrupted me?"

"I believe we were just getting to a most exciting lover," said Nadine, and her eyes were still dancing though she kept her mouth serious and grave. "Was he a brilliant young artist, Grandmother?"

"I'm sorry to disappoint you, dear, but he wasn't. He was only a doctor, a perfectly ordinary country G.P., and I met him through the children's measles."

Nadine and David forbore to smile, for Lucilla spoke with such quiet intensity. She was back in the past now, recapturing deeply-felt emotion, and even the room seemed gathering round to listen as she went on with her story.

"James and I took a house on the Island, our Island that we see from Damerosehay, for the whole summer, because the children had been so ill with measles in the spring. I was there all the time, of course, and James came down for the week-ends. Michael Forbes was the doctor there. The village where we had our house was a quiet little place, and he came in to see us a great deal, as a friend as well as a doctor, because he was lonely. At the beginning I only liked him, but I liked him better than anyone else I had ever met. He was young, just my age, and he cared about all the country things just as I did, but as James did not. James, you know, was always a thorough Londoner, but I was brought up in the country, and I've always hated towns. Michael could ride well and we often went out together. Riding had been the joy of my life before my marriage but James never cared for it; his seat on a horse was a heartbreaking thing. Michael read a lot, too, and though he wasn't actually an artist, Nadine, he had an appreciation of beauty that enriched my life for ever. He could be very amusing and he made me laugh a lot. It was so long since I had really laughed. But best of all he was so sensitive in all his contacts. It was wonderful to see him with a sick child or a frightened little animal. Had he been married I knew he would have been very gentle with his wife, far more gentle than James had ever been with me. There was something about him that seemed to heal the wounds of the mind as well as the body."

"What did he look like?" asked Nadine with eager feminine curiosity. David was a little impatient with her. What on earth, at this immense distance of time, did it matter what the fellow had looked like? Yet in a minute he found that, to him, it most surprisingly did matter.

"He was good to look at," said Lucilla. "I shouldn't have loved him if he hadn't been, for I was hungry for every sort of beauty. He was tall and graceful and he looked his best on horseback; all good-looking men do. He was fair, with very smooth gold hair."

She raised her head suddenly and found her grandson looking at her with most painful intensity. He was almost, she thought, a little white. After a moment's puzzlement she understood. "No, no, my dear," she cried, a little amused in spite of herself. "Don't look like that, David. It never got to that. Your father was James's child, not Michael's. You've every right to the name of Eliot."

David relaxed, a little shamefacedly. Lucilla's eyes, he noticed, were still twinkling. She had caught him out. He, who was all for truth rather than law in human relationships, had, caught unexpectedly, not wanted to find himself with no legal right to his own name . . . He grinned at Lucilla.

"After Grandfather," pronounced Nadine, "you must have fallen for a man like that very badly indeed, Grandmother."

"I did," said Lucilla, "but gradually. There was nothing violent about it. I just woke up one morning to find that in him all my desperate unsatisfied longings were satisfied completely, and that his companionship was the only thing in the world I wanted. This love was, I thought, the one and only really true thing that had ever happened to me. My marriage and motherhood had always seemed like a sort of play that I acted. This was real. It was the same with his love for me. It seemed to him, he told me, the only truth there was. It dwarfed everything else. Even his beloved work seemed an unreal thing beside it. I don't need to explain such a love to you. You know all about it, and how the power of it can numb thought and memory and drive the sanest and best of men and women to the maddest of acts . . . Unless fate gives them a quiet breathing space in which to recollect themselves . . . I had it, and it saved me from doing incalculable harm, and I am hoping that this time at Damerosehay will give it to you."

There was naturally no response to this, and Lucilla went on.

"We arranged to go away together. This was the way one did things in those days. There were none of these arranged divorces," and here her eyes fell upon her daughter-in-law and her voice grew a little hard, "none of this ridiculous business of making the man take the blame as though the fault were his only. In those days, if a woman wanted to leave her husband for another man, she did so openly, and the blame was hers; and very severe blame it was, too; she and the man she went to were socially ruined to an extent that can hardly be understood nowadays." She paused, then went on again. "Looking back after all these years I can understand myself, for I was a selfish creature when I was young, I had next to no religion, I was not happy with my husband and I did not love my children as much as I should have done. But I find it hard to understand Michael, for he was so fine a creature. It is strange to me that he should have been so completely overturned by a silly young woman."

"I can understand him," said David, and his smiling eyes told her how utterly adorable the young Lucilla must have been.

"Don't interrupt, dear, because I cannot remember where I am, if you interrupt . . . Well, we made our plans. We were to go to

32

France. Michael had a little money of his own and on that we planned to live, for we knew, of course, that his professional life would be smashed by what we were doing. James was in London and I told the servants and the children that I was going to him. Michael had established a locum and was supposed to be taking his annual holiday. It seemed quite natural to everybody that we should go down together to catch the morning boat to the mainland. Even now I can recapture the happiness as though it were yesterday. We went down to the boat in Michael's dog-cart, through lanes full of honeysuckle. In spite of days and nights of anxiety and torturing indecision I was half crazy with joy. And then, just as we were getting on the boat, a frantic man came running to say that a favourite patient of Michael's, a little boy of three, had burnt himself most dangerously. They did not trust the locum, they wanted Michael." She paused and sighed, as though even now the memory of that moment oppressed her. "And Michael went. Before I came along he had been mad about his work; the best men always are. He just dumped down his bag and ran down the gangway, calling to me to take a cab home and we'd go by tomorrow's boat, and was off like a flash in his dog-cart before I'd even got time to protest. I was furious, of course. I thought he ought to have left the child to the locum and considered me first. He had put me in a very difficult position. He had, I thought, been very cruel. I did not go home. I was too angry. I put our luggage in the little office on the quay and walked to the nearest bit of seashore and tramped up and down and raged and stormed, and cried until I was utterly exhausted. Then, I think, I must have slept a little. I was worn out and it was quiet and warm in the sunny little bay. Then I sat up and ate my sandwiches and looked across the estuary to the mainland on the other side. I saw the cloud shadows passing over the wide flat marshes and flocks of sea birds wheeling up into the sun. I did not know, of course, that I was looking across at Damerosehay country, but the peacefulness of that wide landscape had a very powerful effect on me. It seemed to clear my mind and lull my torment to sleep so that I was able to think, and to think hard and straight. I stayed there all day, thinking."

She stopped and David, to give her time to rest a bit, went over to a window and pulled the curtain a little to keep the sun out of her eyes. He was touched by her story. Lucilla was such a serene old lady that he had never pictured her torn by any sorrows except those of inevitable bereavement. It astonished him that she too had known passion and conflict. Nadine, he saw, was moved too. He supposed that all human experience is very much the same. We think our own sufferings are unique and then we find that everyone else has been through much the same . . . or worse.

"I want to try and tell you the conclusions I arrived at that day," said Lucilla. "This is what I really want to tell you. My silly little love story isn't really important, and at one time I had not meant to tell it, but the conclusions one comes to about living are important. They mould our lives, and sometimes other people's lives too . . . My thinking all started from the fact, so bitter to me, that Michael had put his work before his love for me. And he had done that instinctively. He had had no time to reason things out, if he had I expect he would have come with me, he had simply acted upon instinct. Now in those days I had great faith in instinct. It was instinct, I thought, that guided the world aright, that sent the wild birds flying across seas and continents to find their home, that taught the animals to care for their young, even to die for them if need be. Instinct, I thought, was the voice of God . . . I still think that very often it is, though I realize now that there is such a mixture of good and evil in all we think and are that everything, every instinct and every thought, needs to be tested by the teaching of Christ . . . And if that were true it meant that Michael, in instinctively putting his work before his love, was doing right. Yet he had said that his love for me seemed a truer, a more real thing, than his work. So great was his love that he had been quite ready to have his work ruined by it.

"That made me think very hard, even as you have thought, David, about the nature of truth. What is it once one moves beyond the narrow conception of truth as the correctly spoken word? You must remember that I had never read very much and that I had to think it out very crudely for myself. I thought it out and I said to myself that true action is the creation of perfection while lying

34

action is the creation of something that falls short of the ideal. 'That is a true line,' we say, when it is drawn as near to the straight as we can get it. 'That is a bad portrait,' we say of a picture that is not like the original. From there I went further and I said that truth at its greatest is something made in the likeness of God."

" 'Beauty is truth, truth beauty',' quoted David softly, smiling at her.

"Yes, dear, but don't interrupt. I was very uneducated, as I said before. I don't believe I had ever read Keats in those days. I had to struggle on by myself to the idea that if truth is the creation of perfection then it is action and has nothing to do with feeling. And the nearest we can get to creating perfection in this world is to create good for the greatest number, for the community or the family, not just for ourselves; to create for ourselves only means misery and confusion for everybody. That made me see that acting a part is not always synonymous with lying, it is far more often the best way of serving the truth. It is more truthful to act what we should feel if the community is to be well served rather than behave as we actually do feel in our selfish private feelings."

"In other words, Grandmother," said David, smiling, "it is more truthful to pretend you love your husband when you don't, rather than run away with another man because you do. That, you think, is the best way of creatively building up the ideal of faithfulness in marriage, which to your mind is a better thing for the community, and therefore a truer thing, than adultery."

"You put it crudely, dear," complained Lucilla.

"Life is a bit crude," agreed David.

"Yes, that's what I thought," said Lucilla. "Only I thought no less about my work for the community as a wife and mother than Michael's as a doctor. I thought all day about his work. A doctor's work is splendidly creative, I thought; building strong bodies and healthy minds; it is more creative even than the work of painter and sculptor for he deals in flesh and blood and thought, materials that are living. It seemed to me appalling, as I thought it over, that all this should be sacrificed to his passion for a pretty woman. It was every bit as bad as that my work for my husband and children should be sacrificed to my passion for a charming man. The love of a man and a woman, I saw, should never be allowed to be an end in itself; it should be the helpmate of their work."

"Do you know, Grandmother," said Nadine gently, "if you could reason this all out so clearly I don't think you could have been so desperately in love as you thought you were."

"Oh, but I was!" said Lucilla, and her tone was so piteous that they had to believe her. "I don't know why it was that I could think so clearly then, for I'm not usually a clear thinker. Perhaps it was the shock of Michael's action. A shock can have two effects, you know; sometimes it stuns you and sometimes it quickens you; I suppose it did the second to me. I had pencil and paper in my bag and sitting on the shore I wrote to Michael, telling him why I could not go with him after all. Then I tore up the letter I had written to James, and had meant to post on the mainland, and threw it in the sea, and I walked quietly home, posting Michael's letter on my way. As I went in at our garden gate Hilary came running to meet me, he was a little boy of eight years old then, and he hugged me. He was so glad I had not gone away after all. 'Don't ever go,' he said. 'No,' I said, 'I won't,' and I cried and hugged him hard. Next day James came back and I told him I was tired of the Island. So we moved and went back to the mainland."

"Were you very unhappy, Grandmother?" asked Nadine.

"For the whole of the next year I was so unhappy that I did not know how to go on living. Every day when I woke up in the morning I used to hope that this day would be my last on earth— I was as unhappy as all that. The fact was that I loved Michael more than all my children put together. It's a dreadful thing to say, but it's true. I did not see how I could live without my best-beloved. But I did, of course, one so often has to. It was Ellen who saved me."

"Ellen?" asked David, astonished.

"Ellen knew all about it, of course; I don't know how because I didn't tell her; perhaps I left a letter about, for I'm very careless. Ellen doesn't think it wrong to read my letters. She thinks it her sacred duty to know all that's going on in the family, no matter by what means. She knew and told me that she knew. She was kind, but stern. 'What you need, Milady,' she said, 'is to love your poor children a bit more.' 'But I do love them,' I protested. 'I have sacrificed my happiness for them.' 'You don't love 'em as much as I do,' said Ellen. 'What you need is to do a bit more for 'em. It's I who do all the work, not you. Never a hand's turn do you do for those children . . . And if I was you, Milady, I should have another.'

"What Ellen said made me think again. I thought, love at its highest, like truth at its highest, is a creative thing. Perhaps it is action, not feeling. I was playing the part of a good wife and mother quite successfully in the outward ways but that, I saw now, was not enough. That was not love. Creative love meant building up by quantities of small actions a habit of service that might become at last a habit of mind and feeling as well as of body. I tried, and I found it did work out like that. Feeling can be compelled by action not quite as easily as action by feeling, but far more lastingly. You may not believe me, but it's true."

They smiled at her, but their faces looked as though blinds had been drawn over them. She had no idea what, if any, effect she was having upon them.

"And the last baby?" asked Nadine. "Maurice? David's father?"

Lucilla's face softened and shone, as it always did at the mention of Maurice. "I took Ellen's advice and I had him," she said. "James had been very upset, not to say outraged by my refusal to have more children. I told him I was sorry and I asked to have another; and, Maurice, as you know, was the glory of my life. After he came living was not only possible but actually happy again. I suppose a psychologist would have said that in my love for Maurice I sublimated my love for Michael. And the odd thing was that though he was not his son Maurice was very like Michael. He had a sensitiveness and a beauty that none of my other children had . . . And yet I suppose it was not so odd for our children are the children of our minds and souls as well as our bodies, and my mind and soul belonged to Michael."

"What happened to Michael?" asked Nadine.

"Nothing dramatic, dear. He just went on with his work. But he never married, and I suppose he was unhappy on the Island after what had happened for he left it and went to the north of England, and later he came to London and before he died he was considered to be one of the greatest child specialists of his day. He must have saved the lives of a multitude of little children. He would never have done that had he married me. When we were both middle-aged I met him once at a London dinner party, and I think I was rather expecting him to tell me that I had broken his heart and ruined his life; not that I thought I had but I thought it would be nice of him to say so. But Michael was never one to say the proper thing if it wasn't the truth. 'Sensible young woman that you were,' he said to me. 'You saved us both from a great disaster.' I asked him, a little wistfully, if he hadn't been upset for a time. 'Just for a twelvemonth,' he said. 'A year of hell, though it seems long at the time, isn't really long compared with the span of a man's working life.' I said no, I supposed it wasn't, and we said good-bye very politely and I never saw him again."

"And Grandfather never knew a thing about it?" asked Nadine.

"Oh no, dear," said Lucilla, horrified at the bare idea.

"How odd of you not to tell him, Grandmother," said David. "Now I couldn't have gone on living with him if I hadn't made a clean breast of it."

"Your Grandfather would have been very upset if I had told him, dear," said Lucilla. "I wanted to tell him, of course, but I saw no reason why he should be upset just to give me peace of mind. Confession is rather a selfish luxury, I think."

David marvelled at her. Inward integrity meant so much to him that her ruthless sacrifice of it to the common good knocked him speechless.

WONDER

JOB'S DELIGHT

THE Dean perceived that Job was about as wretched as a boy could be and he said, "Now we are here together shall we look at those carvings I told you of? The light is growing, I think."

"You are not busy, sir?"

"No, Job. I am quite at liberty and there is nothing I should like better than to show you my Cathedral. I dare to call it mine, and I believe Tom Hochicorn does too. Our presumption appears great but the glory delights to be possessed as well as to possess."

He got up and moved out from the chantry to the nave and Job followed him, at first passively and dumbly as a whipped dog, then with awed self-forgetfulness, and finally with surging excitement. As he walked with the Dean he was almost dancing with the compulsion he had to put upon himself not to outstrip the old man beside him. Who could have told it was like this inside the mountain? Who could have known such glory existed? Why had nobody told him? What a fool he had been not to come inside before! What a fool! If Isaac had felt he had a hawk with him in the workshop the Dean thought first of an eagle, so fierce and strong was the joy beside him, and then of a terrible young archangel, incapable of fatigue, the touch of whose hand against his shivering mortal flesh was a touch of fire. The boy had forgotten there had ever been a clock. All his sorrows were under his flaming feet and his joy set a nimbus about his head. Yet he retained his awe, listening to what the Dean said, glad to the depth of him that it was with this man and no other that he was for the first time in this place.

He would see them all in years to come, Canterbury, York, Ely, Chartres, Notre Dame, San Marco and the golden churches of Palermo, but none of them would exalt and wring him quite as this one did today. The light grew and there were shafts of silver through the gloom. He remembered how he had dreamed of walking in a forest, where from the great-girthed boles of the trees the branches leapt to the sky, and of looking up at the dark stone cliffs of the mountain and wondering what such walls could hold, and of being below the sea where the tides washed in and out of the green gloom of caverns. Marvellous colours glowed in the windows far above him, the deep jewel colours of very old glass. There were lords and ladies here, angels and haloed saints, bishops and knights lying on their tombs, figures such as he had seen in some of Mr. Penny's old books, and fabulous creatures such as lions and unicorns, dolphins and griffins. Sometimes there was music, sounding like wind in the trees or water falling from the heights of the mountain, and sometimes silence and the far sound of a bell. There was dust here, for when he unconsciously put out his hand to feel the shape of a dolphin his long fingers came away coated with the friendly stuff. And under the miserere seats there were homely men and boys and creatures such as he knew, woodcutters and millers and ploughmen and young thieves stealing apples, foxes and owls, and small birds such as he made himself. From these he could not tear himself away. To him they were the best of all. They made him laugh and yet they brought him nearer to weeping than anything else because the men who had made them had been dead for centuries and he could not know these men. The whole world was in this place, the earth, the sky and the sea, angels, men and creatures. He looked up often at the great rood, but that he did not understand, except that it seemed to him that nothing else could have been here without that.

"It is all here," he said.

"It is all here in microcosm," said the Dean. "The whole work of God."

He lowered a miserere seat and sat down, for he was trembling with exhaustion and the saints in the window above him seemed to be emptying buckets of cold water over his head. He hoped he might be forgiven for keeping the tireless Job in ignorance of the existence of the Lady Chapel, the crypt and the chapter house.

The boy was kneeling beside him, his head bent, intent upon a man and two yoked oxen ploughing a field. The furrows of the black fen earth shone as though newly turned and at the ploughman's right a bird was singing in a thorn bush under a high midday

42

sun, as though to cheer the labouring man and toiling beasts. The scene was full of the sense of hard driving effort. Every muscle of man and beasts seemed at full stretch. With his finger-tips he lightly touched the bird, and the ploughman's bent back. "I think it is the best of all," he murmured.

"I think I am most attached to the one I am sitting on," said the Dean. "The shepherd with his sheep. But then I have always wished that I could have been a shepherd. You no longer fear the Cathedral?"

"Not now I know these are here, sir," said Job. "I don't see how anyone could come here for the first time and not be afraid, but then this bird is here and it's no bigger than my thumb." He paused, placing his hands one on each side of the carving. "This is just the one man but the Cathedral is filled with them all."

The Dean was a little startled. "You mean filled with the men who made it?"

"Yes, sir."

The Dean sought about in his battered mind for the words he wanted, and then fell back in relief upon the words of another man. "If you remember, Job, I showed you a bishop with mitre and crosier carved on the capital of a pillar in the south transept and told you he was Saint Augustine, a man born in North Africa in 354, long before a stone of this Cathedral was laid in place. He said this, 'And who is that God but our God, the God who made heaven and earth, who filled them because it is by filling them with himself that he has made them.' Man is made in the image of God and as you said just now what he makes he fills with himself, either with his hate or with his love."

Job did not answer. He sprang lightly to his feet and moved up and down before the long line of exquisite small carvings, as though he could not bring himself to leave them. The Dean got up unsteadily and raised his seat so that Job might look again at the shepherd bringing his sheep home to their fold. He carried a crook and had a dog at his heels and a lamb over his shoulder, and above his head the sickle moon hung in the sky. The scene was as full of peace as the other of stress. The Dean glanced from one to the other and suddenly realized something that he had not noticed

43

before. The toiling ploughman and the peaceful shepherd were the same man. He had the same stooped shoulders, the same tall hat and heavy serf's boots. He was Everyman. He pointed this out to Job.

"Yes, I saw that," said Job. "The same craftsman must have carved both and you can see, sir, that he loved the man."

They walked to the south door in silence but the Dean was well aware of the strong confident vow that Job had made. They thought, these young creatures, that they could bind their passions with their vows and did not know the appalling strength of human passion. Yet it was good that they made them, for under the midday sun the vows were bit and bridle upon the wild horses, and as the day drew on to evening the creatures quietened.

FATHER SPRIGG READS THE BIBLE

WHEN supper was finished Mother Sprigg, Madge and Stella quickly removed the dishes while Father Sprigg, sepulchrally clearing his throat, walked with heavy deliberate tread to the dresser, took the Book from inside the willow pattern soup tureen that was never used except to hold the Book, carried it back to the table and laid it down carefully before his chair. There he seated himself, took off his spectacles, polished them on his scarlet handkerchief, readjusted them on his beak of a nose, wetted his finger and slowly turned the pages until he found the pressed carnation that marked the place. Mother Sprigg, Madge and Stella re-seated themselves about the table with hands reverently folded in their laps, and Sol in his chimney corner cupped his right ear in his hand.

The only books at the farm were the Bible and the family Prayer Book, and Father Sprigg read one chapter of the Bible aloud to his household every evening. He worked solidly through from Genesis to Revelation, taking the difficult words with the same courage with which he took a five-barred gate in the hunting field, charging as fast and furious as his own bull through the more indelicate passages of the Old Testament, happy in the New Testament with the parables of sowing and reaping and harvesting and with the shepherds in the fields, but making his way through the last chapters of the gospels with stumbling tongue, his ears scarlet with distress, humiliated by his inability to read such a story as it should be read, but shirking nothing whatever from the first page of the Book until the last.

What his wife and Madge and Sol made of it all, what he made of it himself, it would have been difficult to say; perhaps to them it was mainly a soporific before bedtime, to him one of those duties which from generation to generation fall to the master of the house and must be performed with constant patience.

But to Stella this nightly reading was glory, enchantment and anguish. Sitting there so demurely, her eyes cast down, her hands folded, she gave no outward sign of her excitement; but the blood drummed in her ears at the old tales of adventure, of battle and murder and sudden death. She was one of the trumpeters who blew their trumpets about the walls of Jericho. She stood with the watchman on the tower and saw the cloud of dust whirl up in the distance and heard him cry aloud the dreadful tidings, "The driving is as the driving of Jehu the son of Nimshi; for he driveth furiously." She held her breath while that splendid wicked woman Jezebel painted her face and looked out of the window to greet her murderer. She mourned with David over Absalom, "Would God that I had died for thee, my son, my son." She listened with Elijah to the still small voice that came after the whirlwind and the fire, she gazed upon the mighty Seraphim with Isaiah, she was with Daniel in the lion's den and with Ruth she wept in the harvest fields so far from home.

The New Testament she could hardly bear, so great was her rage at what they did to Him. She could scarcely enjoy the Baby in the manger, the wise men with their gifts, the little children coming to be blessed and the sick folk to be healed, because of what was coming. This King was crowned with thorns instead of gold, and helpless on a gallows had a kind of royalty and power that she dared not as yet even try to comprehend; she was just sickened and infuriated. She was not much cheered by the Resurrection stories;

45

to her they were ghost stories and they scared her. She had a feeling, now and then, that the part of the Bible which now so frightened her would one day come to mean more than all the rest of the Book put together, but that time was a long way off yet. She recovered herself in the Acts and Epistles, though that was about all she did do, the story-telling there being upon the meagre side, but in the Book of Revelation she was at home again; a child once more in this fairy land of magical beasts and a city built of jewels.

But all through the Book, even in the dreadful parts, the language would now and then suddenly affect her like an enchantment. The peculiarities of Father Sprigg's delivery worried her not at all. It was as though his gruff voice tossed the words roughly into the air, separate particles of no great value, and immediately they fell again transmuted, like the music of a peal of bells or raindrops shot through with sunshine, and vista beyond vista of unobtainable beauty opened before the mind. It was a mystery to Stella that mere words could make this happen. She supposed the makers of these phrases had fashioned them to hold their visions as one makes a box to hold one's treasure, and Father Sprigg's voice was the key grating in the lock, so that the box could be open and set them free. But this metaphor did not take her very far. That transmutation in the air still remained as unexplainable as the sudden change in herself, when at the moment of the magical fall her dull mind became suddenly sparkling with wonder and her spirit leaped up inside her like a bird. She wondered sometimes if the others felt the same. She had never looked to see if their faces changed when the brightness fell from the air; but she did not suppose that they did, nor hers either. And they did not say anything; but then neither did she. This was probably one of those many queer experiences that human beings could not speak of to each other, because though words could be formed into a casket to hold visions, and could be at the same time the power that liberated them, they seemed of very little use when one tried to use them to explain to another person what it was that they had set free. Words were queer things, Stella decided, to be at once so powerful and so weak.

For the past ten days Father Sprigg had been wading through Deuteronomy and Mother Sprigg and Madge had dozed a bit. But not Stella. There had been Og the King of Bashan, the last of the giants, and his vast bedstead. And then there had been the Ammonites who dwelt in the mountains and came out against you and chased you, as bees do, and you returned and wept before the Lord. Og had stalked through Stella's imagination, and the Ammonites had buzzed through it, for days. And now tonight, in the eleventh chapter, the tossed words sparkled and fell and the brightness was with her again. "It is a land of hills and valleys, and drinketh water of the rain of heaven. A land which the Lord thy God careth for; the eyes of the Lord thy God are always upon it, from the beginning of the year even unto the end of the year."

It was her own West Country that Stella saw, with its round green hills dotted with sheep and the streams winding in and out between them, and down in the sheltered valleys the orchards and ploughed fields of rose-red earth, the homesteads and the old grey churches. She saw the sun and rain sweeping over the land, and the great arc of the rainbow in the sky, and it was as though the earth lifted itself to drink of the sun and the rain, and even as she watched the corn sprang green in the furrows, the orchards frothed with blossom, and the perfume of many flowers and the singing of a multitude of birds rose up like incense to the God Whose eyes, looking upon it, had given life. There was a reverse side to the picture, a terrible one. If God were to weary and glance away that would be the end of light and life; darkness and chaos would come again. But then God did not weary. From the beginning of the year until the end of the year the light of His eyes streamed down and the life of the earth streamed up. Dazzled, Stella saw the light and life meeting, mingling, looked again and saw her familiar countryside slowly transformed by the union, saw it become another country, the same yet different, the symbol becoming the actual, the shadow reality, the dream the fact of the promised land.

The brightness faded and for the first time she looked at the others. It was old Sol whom she looked at first and his attitude had changed. He was leaning sideways, to bring his ear and cupped

47

hand close to Father Sprigg's voice, and he had lifted his head a little, as a man does who looks at a distant view. Then she looked at Mother Sprigg and Madge. Mother Sprigg was dozing and Madge's face wore the curiously vacant look that it always had when she was not engaged in the active work that was her life. Then she looked back again at old Sol and this time, feeling her gaze, he looked at her, and he smiled and she smiled. So old Sol saw things too. Of course. She ought to have known. That chant with which he kept the oxen moving so rhythmically had made its way into this world from another country.

Father Sprigg closed the Book and they all bent their heads while he repeated the Lord's Prayer. "Amen!" said Father Sprigg in a voice like a thunderclap when he got to the end. Then he let out a great gusty sigh of relief and profound self-satisfaction, inflated his chest and squared his shoulders. Once more he had performed an uncongenial duty creditably and the mingled feelings of martyrdom and virtue that it gave him were pleasantly inflating to the ego. Mother Sprigg rubbed the sleep out of her eyes and intelligence dawned again in Madge's face as she got up to set the table for breakfast.

WILLIAM AND MARIANNE'S TREASURE

"AN' now ye'd best be gettin' home," said Captain O'Hara. "Ye've respectable homes, I can see by the look of you, an' there'll be the divil an' all to pay if ye're not in 'em in an hour or so."

He walked to the curtain of golden dragons, pulled it back and disclosed his curtained bunk and an old battered sea chest. He lifted the lid of the chest, rummaged in it and took out two packages. Then he cleared the breakfast things on to the floor, laid the packages on top of the teak table and opened them. One was an exquisite little carved box containing a pair of beautifully shaped earrings of green stone, and the other was a knife with a carved handle and a carved wooden case to protect it. The carving on both

48

box and knife was simple but lovely, with curves and arabesques beautifully interlaced.

"From New Zealand," said Captain O'Hara. "You wouldn't think murderin' heathen could do work like that, would you? But ye don't need virtue to be an artist, seemingly." He handed the box with the earrings to Marianne. "Take a look at 'em, me dear. They're made of a stone called tangiwai. Green's your colour, I see. The Maoris use a knife like that, son, for cutting up fish and human flesh. You feel that edge. Men find a knife like that come in handy."

They held the treasures in their hands and for a moment they were speechless. William felt the keen edge of the knife with a cautious forefinger while he held the handle in his other hand. The rough carved surface of it fitted well into the palm and helped one to get a good grip. Right on the other side of the world, thousands of miles away, the brown hand of a cannibal had held this knife. A thrill went through him, half pleasant, half horrible, as though the brown hand were holding his across the world, dragging at him, pulling, compelling.

Lying in the palm of her hand the beautiful green earrings lay and looked at Marianne. They were a clear, almost transparent green, with beautiful markings in them like ferns and fishes. Gazing at them Marianne thought there would be nothing you could not see in them, as fortune-tellers do in crystals. Yes, they were her favourite colour, elfin-green, the green of a curving wave on a grey day, undismayed though the sky is clouded, a brave colour; not the sort of exciting brave colour that scarlet is, flashing and flaming and soon burnt out, but cool and keen, quiet, the colour that even in mid-winter is never quite banished from the earth and that shows first through the melting snow, the best and most tenacious colour in the whole world. Her brown fingers closed over the treasures and her black eyes looked straight into Captain O'Hara's. "I'll have my ears pierced this morning," she said with finality.

NAT RUNS AWAY

THE little boy called Nat had never as far as he knew had any other name, Nat told Véronique. He lived in the city of London and swept chimneys. He supposed he'd had a father and mother but he couldn't remember them. Both past memories and present experience consisted only of soot, and having sore eyes and being beaten by his master, and playing in a back yard with two other boys who got beaten too, and washing the nasty mess on their backs for them with water from a pump, and giving them most of his food because they were always hungrier than he was. He was a thin and bony boy and very ugly, and it is well known that the ugly don't have such hearty appetites as the beautiful. Chimneys in London in those days were great towers of stone with steps inside and little boys climbed up them to sweep the soot away. It was a long painful climb, and Nat himself was always glad when at last he saw a patch of blue sky overhead, with sometimes the wings of birds passing across it, and gladder still to get right to the top, put his head out and look at all the hundreds of chimneys stretching away to the skyline, with thin mangy cats yowling about between them. He was devoted to these cats. He always gave them an encouraging word and made it his business to collect fish-heads out of the gutters for them. His pockets were always full of these stinking delicacies and the difficult painful business of sweeping a chimney was alleviated for him by the thought of what he would be able to do for the cats when he got to the top.

The little Nat did not know that there was anything in London, or the world either for that matter, except chimneys; he thought they just went on and on for ever. And then one fine spring morning he suddenly wondered if they did. He wondered if there were other things to see in the world besides chimneys, other things to do besides clean them. He wondered so much that quite suddenly one morning, without in the least realizing that he was going to do it, he ran away. It was not to escape from the beatings and the sore eyes that he ran away, because it was not in his nature to run away from things, but simply to see what there was in the world besides chimneys. And he would not have gone, of course, had the other two boys whose backs he had washed, and to whom he had given most of his food, not caught the fever and died, because it was not his habit to leave anyone who wanted him. It was true that the cats wanted him, but he suspected that cats were everywhere, like the sparrows to whom he gave the last crumb of his crusts, and that he'd be just as useful to other cats as to these. So there being nothing to keep him off he went and found to his astonishment that there was a great deal in the world besides chimneys. To begin with there were the streets of London below the chimneys. He had known they were there before, of course, but he had only trod them in the half dark going to work, or coming back from work when he had been too tired to notice anything. Now, exploring them in the full brilliance of a spring day, he found them full of wonder. There were barrel organs in them and the scent of lilac, and grand ladies and gentlemen bowling along in fine carriages, and people of all sorts and shapes and sizes walking along on foot, and shop windows and crossing sweepers and boot-blacks. All that spring and summer he lived in these glorious streets, picking up a living holding the heads of horses. He simply adored these horses, and besides collecting fish-heads for the cats he also collected apple cores for the horses. They loved him and he was so clever at keeping them quiet that his services were in per-petual demand, and sometimes he earned enough to buy a whole stale cod at the fishmonger's for the cats, or a whole apple for his favourite horse. By night he slept in any corner he could find, with the cats. This was not so good because in the summer of England it was sometimes cold and wet, but he did not grumble about it because it was the price he had to pay for knowing about the wonderful streets. He knew instinctively that pain is the price you pay for knowing about things, and so as he liked to know about things it was no good grumbling.

And then one fine autumn morning it suddenly occurred to him to wonder if walking along a street or bowling along it in a carriage was the only way of getting about the world. Did a street just go on for ever or did it sometimes turn into something else? And if it did turn into something else what was this something else and where did it take you? Obviously the only way of answering these questions was to start walking along a street and to go on and on in the same direction and see what happened.

So very early one morning he put a crust of bread and an apple core into his pocket and started walking eastward into the dawn. He said to himself that if he kept the rising sun in front of him always then he would keep straight and not go round and round in circles. He chose a narrow cobbled street, with high walls on either side. There had been rain in the night, but the sky was clear now, and the rising sun made the cobbles gleam and shine like the jewels that he had seen in the shop windows, and turned the high wet walls to sheets of gold. This was suddenly not London any more. It was not even in the old world that he had hitherto known. It was a new world altogether. He had often wondered how far London stretched but he had not known it was as easy as all this to step out of. He walked on and on into the sun for what seemed like hours but he was so excited that he did not get weary at all.

And then the miracle happened and the street turned abruptly into something else, turned with such startling suddenness that he nearly fell headlong down a flight of steps into the new sort of street that he had turned into. For it was still a street, going along at right angles to the houses on the other side, but it was a street that moved, a street composed of brilliant flashing liquid diamonds, flowing and rippling under the sun. He had never been so astonished in all his life. He just stood there and gaped. And then he stopped gaping and laughed, because he knew in his soul that the discovery of this new sort of street was the most wonderful discovery that he would ever make in all his life.

He went down the steps and cautiously felt the rippling diamonds with his dirty bare foot, and they were cold and wet like rain, and soft, and it was not possible to stand upon them. And then he knew that this new sort of street was composed entirely of water, that it was a gigantic edition of one of the streams that ran down the London gutters after a thunderstorm. But if one could not stand on it how did one get anywhere upon it? He straightened himself and looked about him and found to his stupefaction that houses were floating on it as he had seen bits of paper floating upon the streams in the gutters. They were odd-shaped houses, with small round windows in their wooden walls, and immensely tall thin chimneys going up at a slant, with washing hanging out between them. But no, they weren't chimneys, they were wooden poles, and the washing did not look so much like washing as immense birds' wings. Did these wooden houses fly? There was one not far away from him, quite near to the stone wall that bounded the water-street upon the one side, and a plank was leaning at a steep slant from the wall to its roof. It was the work but of a moment for Nat to run down that wall and nip up that plank.

BEAUTY

NELSON'S FLEET AT SUNSET

O N a clear August evening, borne upon the light breath of a fair wind, the fleet was entering Torbay. The sight was so lovely that the men and women in the fishing villages grouped about the bay gazed in wonder, and stilled the busyness of their lives for a moment to stand and watch, shielding their eyes with their hands, trying each in their own way, consciously or unconsciously, to imprint this picture upon their memories so deeply that it should be for them a treasure while life should last.

Since England had been at war with Napoleonic France the fleet was often in Torbay. Admiral Hardy in the *Victory* had known the bay well. Admiral Rodney had sailed from Torbay to the Battle of the Saints. Three times in one year the Earl of St. Vincent had anchored in the bay; and Nelson had visited him here. Yet none of these stately comings and goings had had quite the unearthly beauty of this quiet unobtrusive arrival of two ships of the line and four frigates, just at the penultimate moment of the most glorious sunset of the year.

The last light of the sun was streaming over the rampart of green hills to the west, brimming the leafy valleys with liquid gold, then emptying itself in a sort of abandonment of glory into the vast domed space of sky and sea beyond. There were ripples on the water, and a fragile pattern of cirrus clouds above, and these caught the light in vivid points of fire that were delicate as filigree upon the fine metal of the gold-washed sea and sky. There was no sound anywhere. Voices were stilled upon sea and shore and the white gulls with their gold-tipped wings floated silently. The half-moons of golden water, swung and withdrawn so rhythmically by the ebbing tide, creamed soundlessly upon the golden sand, and the tiny sound of the ripples lapping against the jetties and the hulls of fishing boats was lost in the great silence. Into this vast peace, this clear light, sailed the great ships, and for the one unforgettable moment seemed to gather beauty to them as the sun gathers the dew.

Each oak hull, so cumbrous yet so beautiful in motion, was aglow from the ruddy gleam of the copper sheathing just above the water line to the lemon yellow of the lower gun decks. The painted poops, the gilded stern works and figureheads, the glazed cabin ports, winked and sparkled, yet the bright hulls were almost eclipsed by the soaring beauty of the raking masts, and the swell of the great sails that caught the gold light in their curves as delicately as flowers do, yet had so terrible a strength. Flags fluttered from each foremast, mainmast and mizzen, and in the wake of each ship the white foam shone like snow.

AN EIGHTEENTH-CENTURY KITCHEN

THE candle flames and the flames of the burning apple logs, having it all their own way now, seemed to breathe and grow like living creatures and slowly and triumphantly the grand old kitchen came into its own. By day the business of the farm filled it with bustle and clamour, and the bright gay world outside the windows challenged attention, and soon there would be the weight of dreams and darkness on its life, but this pause between the one and the other, between the day and the night, the work and the sleep, was its hour. Stella, looking up, saw the kitchen and recognized a friend coming towards her. The kitchen, to her, was the face of the house, that expressed its personality more accurately than did the walls and roof and chimneys that she thought of as its body, and at this hour the face smiled and she knew as much as she would ever know about Weekaborough Farm, the rugged, strong old creature that was her home, her fortress and her friend.

The kitchen was the living-room of the farm, for they scarcely used the small panelled parlour upon the other side of the flagged hall. It was a large room, roughly square, but with many nooks and bulges, like a cave, two wide mullioned windows with deep window-seats in the long west wall, and one smaller one to the south. The walls were whitewashed and the whitewashed ceiling was crossed by strong oak beams with iron hooks in them for the hams and bunches of herbs to hang from. The furniture, the huge kitchen table, the tall dresser, the settle and the straight-backed chairs, were of oak, shiny and black with age. The stone flagged floor was snowily white from centuries of scrubbing, and under the kitchen table were the pails of water that were kept filled from the big well in the yard.

But the greatest glory of the kitchen was the fireplace that filled nearly the whole of the north wall and was almost a room in itself. It was so deep that there was room for seats on each side, while across the opening in front was a sturdy oak beam with a little red curtain hanging beneath it. The wood fire never went out, winter or summer. Each morning Father Sprigg, always the first downstairs, would rake the ashes together, put on fresh dry wood and blow up the sparks with the bellows. On each side of the fire were firedogs to hold the spits for roasting, and swinging cranes for the pots and kettles. Delicious smells were creeping out now from the fireplace; onion broth cooking in the pot that hung from one of the cranes and apples roasting in a dish placed under the outer ashes of the fire.

All the crannies and bulges of this enchanting cave-like room had unexpected things in them; the bread oven in the thickness of the wall, underneath its fascinating little arch, the grandfather clock, Mother Sprigg's spinning wheel, the warming pans, secret cupboards filled with home-made wines (and in the very secret cupboards, under the fireplace seats, and in recesses made by removing a few stones from the wall, something even stronger), shelves piled with pickles and preserves, brass candlesticks and Toby jugs. The window-seats in the west wall lifted up and inside one of them Stella kept her sampler, and her few treasures, and in the other Mother Sprigg kept her workbox and the current patchwork quilt. Stella had no workbox and the lack of it was the one and only grievance of her life. She longed for one with little compartments in it, and an emery cushion and a real silver thimble. But Mother Sprigg said that until she could sew a bit better she must be content with her tiny hussif and brass thimble. Stella was quite sure that if she had a workbox, and a silver thimble, she would immediately sew beautifully.

THE CHAPEL IN THE PILGRIM INN

THE Chapel was the important thing just now. A friend of John Adair's, an expert, had been down to see the frescoes and had shown them what to do, and now John Adair and David, Ben and Sally, worked increasingly at the restoration of the walls, removing the dirt of ages from the glowing colours below. The frescoes were incredibly lovely. The background of the wood had been painted with a lavishness and eagerness that were astonishing, but, to Ben's delight, the artist's perspective and anatomy were as poor as his own, and he had bothered no more than a child would have done about any kind of likelihood. He had had no hesitation whatever in expressing his passionate love of trees, birds, animals, butterflies and flowers in such a welter of them as took the breath away. He had splashed the trees of Knyght-wood on the walls in all the splendour of their summer foliage, the knotted strength of their roots holding firmly to a green, mossy earth sown thickly with all his favourite flowers, bees, and butter-flies hovering over them and sipping their honey, regardless of season or soil or habitat or anything whatever, except a desire to paint, for the glory of God, every flower and insect that God had made that he could manage to get into the space at his disposal.

It was Ben's guess that he had started with the flowers and butterflies, and then found himself left with no space on the floor of the wood for the birds and animals. But he had not let this worry him. Up above, in every small break in the foliage of the trees, where one expected to see a patch of sky, one saw instead a little leaf-framed picture of an animal or bird enjoying itself. One showed a gull in flight, another a swan sailing on a patch of blue water. There was a deer feeding, a little doe fast asleep, a king-fisher diving for a fish, a robin building a nest, an owl in contemplation, a badger's holt with the back view of the badger going in, a rabbit's burrow with the front view of a rabbit coming out, a squirrel eating nuts, a field mouse sitting up on its hind legs and washing its ears, and as many others as there were frames in the trees in which to put them. There was no sky anywhere, because there was no space in which to put it; but the whole scene shone with so clear and lovely a light, so tranquil and yet so glowing, that one knew that the hot blue of a midsummer day was passing to a golden sunset, with a breath of coolness stirring in the wood and the birds' voices rising in a paean of praise.

Through the wood rode Placidus on his white horse with its golden trappings, Placidus in his poppy-red jerkin and blue cloak, with his dogs about him. Any danger that the brilliance of the wood might have dwarfed the splendour of Placidus was got over by making the man, the horse and the dogs bigger than life-size in comparison with the wood. And there was another striking contrast between the figures of the story and the background against which they moved. The flowers and all the little creatures up in the trees had a strange stillness. They weren't going anywhere. They had reached their moment of completion and stopped there. But the dogs were stretched out in full chase; the horse, suddenly reined in from the gallop, was pawing the ground; Placidus, though for the moment still in awe and wonder, was taut as a bent bow; the whole group was vibrant with eagerness and urgency, a complete contrast both to the stillness of the wood and the stillness of the images upon the east wall.

It was a shock to turn from the jostling brilliance of the wood to the austere splendour of the east wall. The great immobile figure of the deer, white and shining, holding the crucifix aloft between its antlers, had behind it no flowery background, but the bare slope of a purple mountain. Though it was still day in the wood, night was falling on the mountain; darkness veiled it, and far up beyond the topmost peak a few stars shone. But they gave little light. The stag glowed by virtue of the light that shone from the Figure on the cross, a radiance so bright that the actual outline of the Figure was lost in it. The stillness of those images was quite different in quality from the stillness of the wood. It was the stillness not of completion, but of depth. Looking at them was like looking over the edge of a boat down into a calm sea; one knew that far beyond the limit of one's vision were unimaginable things.

And all this had been hidden for years beneath layers of dirty wallpaper. Their awe deepened the longer they worked, and their happiness, too. The thought of this glory, waiting here for so long for re-birth, hidden but safe, was invigorating in these days of anxiety and fear.

THE GLORY OF SAIL

SUDDENLY her hands dropped from her ears, she gave a cry of delight, opened the window wide and leaned out. The *Green Dolphin* was moving. The wind was favourable and she was bound for the port of Bristol.

And Marianné's spirit was with her as she went. Though she was too far away to see the clipper as anything but a beautiful toy at a distance yet in imagination she could hear and see it all. She could see Captain O'Hara upon the poop, red-faced, magnificent, bellowing his orders. She could see the sad monkey face and the twisted smile of Nat beneath his red cap, and hear the men singing at the capstan as they wound up the anchor. And she could hear the creaking of the cordage and the ripple of water along the ship's side, and see the arrow-shaped white water speeding away from the proud curve of the moving prow. And now the clipper was outside the harbour and Marianne felt in her own body the great lift of the ship as the sea took her.

She hung out of the window and watched till her eyes ached, her pulses leaping as one sail after another blossomed like flowers on the masts. Ah, but she was lovely, that ship, the loveliest thing in all the world! And now she was running swiftly before the wind, a wake of white foam behind her. She was like a bird now, like a speeding gull, her wings alight in the sunlight, alive from prow to stern, in every fibre of her, a creature spun out of sun and air, free and indestructible, the spirit of the sea.

Marianne watched for a long while, yet it seemed but a moment. Now the clipper was hull down over the horizon, and now, like petals falling, her sails dropped one by one from sight. A mast-tip gleamed in the sunlight and then she was gone, a dream, an immortal memory, the loveliest thing that earth could give.

THE CLIFFS ABOVE NOTRE DAME

WILLIAM gasped. They were at an immense height above the sea, gazing down at an amphitheatre of rock that took one's breath away. Pinnacles and bastions and towers of grey granite fell away before them, grand and terrible, though softened by the wheeling white wings of gulls and by patches of turf between the rocks where withered heather and bracken took on almost the colour of flame beneath the sun, and by grey veilings of old-man's-beard. Far down below in the bay a crescent of pale golden sand was slipping from beneath an almost transparent veil of blue water, like the moon from beneath a gauzy cloud. Sharp jagged rocks covered with seaweed were showing above the water, and the rocky island of Marie Tape-Tout, standing out to sea beyond the rocks, looked nearer than it was.

"The tide is going out," said Marianne.

To the right of the bay, the great rocks withdrew a little and here was the little fishing village of Notre Dame, the whitewashed cottages sheltering within the crevasses of the cliff, their thatch kept secure against winter storms by netting and rope weighed down by stones. Smoke coiled up from their chimneys, and a few fishing boats, their hulls painted blue and green, lay peacefully upon the quiet water.

But to the left of the bay the rocks soared to a great height and crowning their summit was the Convent of Notre Dame du Castel. Built of grey granite like the rocks below it, weathered by centuries of sunshine and storm, it was now a part of the cliff. It was hard to remember that men had built it; even those almost legendary monks who so long ago had crossed the sea in their frail boats to bring the knowledge of the love of God to the Island savages. They had built well. Notre Dame du Castel reared itself above the Atlantic with a primeval power and strength that made it look more like a fortress than a convent. Marianne told the awe-struck William that in the early days of its history the monks had kept a light always burning in the west window of the great tower of the church, so that by night as well as by day Notre Dame du Castel should be a beacon for mariners for miles across the sea. That tradition had never been allowed to die, and today the nuns still tended the light. Just below the window where it shone, within an alcove cut in the west wall of the tower, a life-size statue of the Madonna stood looking out to sea.

"There's not another convent like it anywhere," said Marianne. "It's famous, you know, all over the world."

LA BAIE DES PETITS FLEURS

JUST at that moment a beautiful white gull sailed by over her head and drifted down into La Baie des Petits Fleurs. The sun touched his feathers to silver as he alighted there upon the little beach and he seemed to be beckoning to her. Marianne and William were absorbed in limpets. They did not see her pick up her blue skirts and skim away over the wet sand towards the forbidden spot.

The bay was farther away than she thought, and ran deeper into the cliff than she had expected. It was shaped like a horse-shoe, and as she ran in between the great rocks that guarded it at the narrow end she understood why this little bay was dangerous, for the high tide watermark on them was well above her head. When she got inside, with the great cliffs towering above her, she felt as alone as though she were the only human being alive upon the Island. But it was a pleasant kind of loneliness, not the sort when one has been pushed out by someone else, but when one has chosen oneself to be alone, the kind when one is less conscious of human creatures having gone away than of listening for the voices and the footsteps of faerie creatures trooping in.

Friendly faerie creatures. The bay was alive with peaceful friendliness. Yet at first she was too much awed by the beauty of this exquisite haunted place to move or to touch, she could only stand quite still and breathe it in as she looked about her. The bay was very small and the cliffs so high that it seemed their rocky crests must touch the sky, and the light that shone from the west through the narrow opening of the horse-shoe came as though flooding into a cavern. She had to tilt her head back before she could see the grey mass of the convent right up overhead, so high that it looked more as though it had been let down from heaven than built up from earth, with the Madonna in her niche, and below her the locked door opening up a narrow sort of shelf in the cliff carpeted with green grass. Le Creux des Fâies, where it was said the fairies feasted round a flat rock at the full of the moon, was to the left of the bay, the narrow entrance half blocked by a big boulder covered with bright green weed. Most of the floor of the bay was covered with fine silver sand and beautiful small stones tinted like opals, with bigger rocks draped with deep purple-brown weed where the rock pools were full of the frilly kind of sea anemones. All the pebbles seemed to Marguerite to have fat smiling faces, and the anemones had mad bright eyes above their frills. At the far end of the bay the sand ran upwards into a hollow in the cliff, almost a second little bay to which the sea did not reach, and here it was carpeted with small coloured shells as a wood is carpeted with flowers in spring-time. And all the shells had mouths and all of them were singing, their myriad tiny voices making a music that one could hear and yet not hear, like the sound of bells that the wind is always catching away. There was not one of them that was bigger than the nail of a baby's finger, and some of them were no larger than a pin's head, but each was as intricately and perfectly fashioned as though it were a world all to itself. Some had the beautiful shape of wool upon the distaff, tapering to a fine point. Others were like rose petals delicately hollowed. Some were like the caps of elves, and others like drops of dew. And each cup or spiral had its own perfect veining of feather-light radiation, each line perfect in grace, drawn by a brush that had never faltered. And their pale flower-tints were as varied as their shapes; lemon flushed with salmon pink, dove grey lined with mother-of-pearl, pale amethyst powdered with green points of fire, saffron and turquoise and rose, and smoky-orange spotted with pale warm brown like the breast of a small bird. And there were no two of them just the same.

The seagull was sailing backwards and forwards all the time, seeming to gather all the light of the place with his shining wings and to trail it in long threads of silver after him as he flew this way and that, very high up between the rocks as though weaving a pattern in the air, filament by filament of light from cliff to cliff. Marguerite stood quite still and watched him, her hands behind her back. There was a legend on the Island that souls in prayer can take the form of a bird and hover over those they pray for, and she wondered if it were true. The silver pattern that he had woven in the air seemed suspended from cliff to cliff over her head like an invisible protection, like one of those canopies powdered with stars that one sees in old pictures held over the heads of Queens as they walk in procession.

It was this sense of protection that at last broke the spell of awe that held her without movement for so long. With a cry of delight she ran and fell on her knees beside the little shells and picked them up one by one, holding them up towards the west so that the sun shone through them and lit their fragile shapes to dazzling fire. Then she picked them up by handfuls, letting them fall again through her brown fingers, as children scoop up water in their hands to see the bright drops fall.

THE FACE OF REVEREND MOTHER

REVEREND Mother's face softened and she looked down intently into the childish face raised to hers. Very few people could meet Reverend Mother's eyes, but Marguerite could. She had never seen anyone quite like Reverend Mother and she was interested. She had seen lots of old ladies with wrinkled parchment faces like Mère Madeleine's, and many round red peasant faces such as Soeur Angelique's, but never a face like this one. Reverend Mother had a clear olive skin, without colour yet almost luminous in its purity, with a beautiful pencilling of fine clear lines about her grey eyes with their brilliant keen glance like the thrust of steel. Her eyebrows were dark and delicate, with one deep line of concentration strongly marked between them. But there were no lines of anxiety on her broad low forehead, and no laughter lines about her resolute tight-lipped mouth. But if her lips were resolute, they were also lovely, as perfectly modelled as the aquiline nose with the winged nostrils, and the strong and delicate chin. And the oval of her face was flawless in its framework of snow-white linen. A beautiful, humourless face, cold with its clamp of iron control set upon its passion, yet alight with holiness; a powerful, brilliant, frightening face. Reverend Mother was tall and held herself superbly, and her habit became her long and supple limbs. It was impossible to tell how old she was. One would have guessed that many embattled years had gone to the making of a face like hers, yet her lovely hands, strangely indolent hands that she held loosely linked before her, were those of a woman still young.

So they stood, the nun and the child, each in characteristic attitude, fearlessly, the one with linked hands before her, the other with her hands clasped behind her back, and they did not know why it was that their eyes so held each other and so questioned.

THE BEAUTY OF NATURE

THE beauty of England had from afar stabbed him now and then with a flash of sunlight, a phrase of bird song, but he had left her before he could become acquainted with her loveliness, and he had been too preoccupied with the saving of souls for the beauty of New Zealand to touch him very nearly. But now, as the great trees of the primeval forest closed about him, shutting away past and future, leaving him with nothing but a couple of saddle-bags, a horse and his bare existence, the earth his mother for the first time held out her arms and pulled him close. As with his spirit in the deeps of prayer so now with his body in her arms, separateness vanished. The same ecstatic life that pulsed in his body throbbed also in the body of his horse, blazed in the sunlight, chimed in the bird song all about him, sang in the wind in the tree-tops, aspired in the delicate veining of leaves and grasses and the silent miraculous unfolding of the flowers. He was in them and they in him, and yet he was still himself and still in some sense hungry; that did not surprise him, for he had learned in prayer that union is not sameness and that in this world the core of longing is never satisfied; what did surprise was the sense of awe and reverence that possessed him, reverence that he had felt hitherto only for God. Reverence for a flower petal that would be dust tomorrow? For a repetitive bird phrase, the opening bars of a statement that was always left unfinished? For such trivialities? And, as in prayer, reverence brought peace and peace dedication. "Then shall the dust return to the earth as it was and the spirit shall return unto God Who gave it." Almost he could imagine that in the supreme self-giving of death there could be as great an exultation in the surrender of the body to the earth as in the surrender of the soul into the hands of God the Father. For the first time in his life he considered earth the mother. Most grievously had he hitherto neglected her. Never had he commented upon the different facets of her beauty as a good son should. Had he said they were trivial a moment ago? The scales as yet had scarcely fallen from his eyes. Stray phrases began to float from him to Tai Haruru, once more like drifting leaves, and Tai Haruru, though paying little attention, yet answered with a comprehension born of his own experience.

"One seems never to catch a flower at the moment of unfolding."

"Flowers are alive, man," murmured Tai Haruru. "You can't watch life, it's divine. The movement of divinity has so miraculous and perfect a rhythm that it is beyond human perception. Smack one man-made brick upon another and you can watch the wall grow; but it is not alive."

"The birds do not finish it," complained Samuel at another time. "They perpetually repeat the question but they give no answer."

"Like all religious men you read more into a thing than its content," said Tai Haruru. "That bird phrase is not the opening bar of a symphony but a lyric, a thing complete in itself. And earth neither asks nor answers questions. Why should she? She herself is finality."

"There is no finality," reiterated Samuel quietly. And indeed he recognized none in this new-found beauty of earth the mother. Every sensual experience of her loveliness was coming to him not as an end in itself but as the shadow of a hint about something beyond comprehension or definition, greeting him as the perfume of a rose growing round the bend of the road would greet a traveller who had never seen a rose. "We have both been unworthy sons of earth," he said to Tai Haruru. "I unobservant of her beauty, you of the purpose of it."

"Laziness?" suggested Tai Haruru lightly. "Too much trouble to take a country walk? Too much bother to pursue the will-o'-the-wisp of beauty to some probably quite imaginary bourne?"

"And pride," said Samuel. "The overweening pride of thinking ourselves capable of a discovery that is sufficient. Enough, you said, when I found my God in prayer. For both of us it has been as though Columbus stopped short in mid-ocean, or Christ turned back at the entrance to Gethsemane."

"Cowardice too then," mocked Tai Haruru. And then he fell into a muse. He knew himself to be a proud man and he knew, too, that there was a streak of indolence in him. But a spiritual coward? He had not suspected that. Was disillusionment another name for cowardice? Perhaps. Yes, most certainly, for it was the line of least resistance... Discouraged... No more despicable epithet could be applied to a man, and yet men often applied it to themselves and felt no shame.

They rode on through the magical beauty of the forest, through murmurous sunlit days and star-hung nights of peace, through song and silence and a web of colour that was like the song and the silence made visible in interwoven strands of dark and light. Their ears could catch only a few notes of music that by day streamed upwards from the teeming earth and by night blazed in the sky in a thousand points of light, but they were a little quicker to catch the notes of colour that matched each note of sound. They had the illusion that there was more to see than to hear, but they were sufficiently humbled now to know that they were wrong. Human eyes are less lazy adventurers than human ears. And from Samuel's eyes the scales had just fallen, leaving them as the eyes of a child, while Tai Haruru's eyes had been those of a painter and craftsman from the beginning.

It was perhaps the sense of danger ahead that gave such a passionate intensity to their experience of earth's loveliness upon this journey. At the back of both their minds was the knowledge that contact with loveliness through the medium of the physical senses was one that might soon have to be laid aside for ever; for another; or nothing.

DELIGHT

THE CELESTIAL CLOCK

THE clock that Isaac was making now he did not visualize in his shop window because it was so much a part of him that he could have as easily visualized his eyes or brain or hands in the window as this clock. He did not think about its future because it was the future. He did not consciously tell himself that it was his eternity but he had a confused idea that the dark would not entirely get him while the pulse beat on in this clock.

Standing before the solid oak table which was sacred to his clock alone his heart beat high with joy at what he saw. No one else would have seen anything except a confused jumble of mechanism, but Isaac saw his clock as it would be. He saw the accomplished thing and knew that he would make it, and that it would be his masterpiece. Like all creators he knew well that strange feeling of movement within the spirit, comparable only to the first movement of the child within the womb, which causes the victim to say perhaps with excitement, perhaps with exasperation or exhaustion, "There is a new poem, a new picture, a new symphony coming, heaven help me." The movement had been unusually strong when he first knew about this clock.

It was to be a lantern clock in the style of the late seventeenth century, the kind of timepiece Tompion himself had so delighted to create, the clock face surmounted by a fret that hid the base of the bell above. Isaac nearly always used the traditional eastern counties fret, a simple design that he liked, but for this clock he was designing his own, inspired by the famous Gothic fret which Tompion had been so fond of, only instead of the two dolphins and the flowers and fruit he saw two swans and the beautiful arrow-head reeds that grew upon the river bank outside the city wall. Isaac could paint on ivory with the skill of a miniaturist, and his clock face was to be a dial of the heavens. The twelve hours were to be the twelve signs of the zodiac, painted small and delicate in the clearest and loveliest colours he could encompass. Each picture lived already in his mind, completely visualized down to the last scale on the glittering fish at twelve o'clock and the golden points of the little shoes the Virgin wore peeping from beneath her blue cloak at six o'clock. Within this circle of stars Isaac had planned the sun and moon balancing each other against a blue sky scattered over with tiny points of light that were the humbler stars, but whenever he stood and looked at his clock the sun would not stay where he wanted it, as did the moon, but swam upwards and placed itself like a golden halo behind the fish. Again and again Isaac had replaced the sun floating just off shore from nine o'clock, but it was no good, it always went back to the meridian. And so now Isaac had given up and as he looked at his clock tonight he acknowledged the rightness of what he saw. The glittering silver fish and the golden sun formed one symbol, though of what he did not know. His heart beat fast and music chimed in his head. The bell of this clock was to strike the half hour as well as the hour, for according to tradition the spheres were singing spirits. "There's not the smallest orb which thou beholdest but in his motion like an angel sings." Isaac did not believe it but he had the kind of mind that delights to collect the pretty coloured fragments of old legends that lie about the floor of the world for the children to pick up. As man and craftsman he knew that he would touch the height of his being with the making of this clock. He covered the lovely thing with a cloth and turned away. It was hard to leave it even though there was nothing under the cloth except a medley of bits of metal and some oily rags.

JOB DELIGHTS THE DEAN

"THE Dean would be much obliged if you would wind the Jeremiah Hartley. Come away, young man, as soon as you have done so."

"Thank you, sir," said Job. He walked to the study door, knocked and entered.

The Dean was writing at his littered table. "Good morning, Job," he said.

"Good morning, sir," said Job, and came up to the table. "I hope you are better, sir?"

"I am quite recovered. How are you, Job? How is your ankle?"

"It has mended, sir. I am very happy working for Mr. Peabody and I like living with Mr. Penny and Ruth."

"You like Ruth?"

"Yes, sir." He paused. "I would like to thank you, sir."

The strong beat of profound happiness was in Job's quietly spoken words. It seemed to the Dean's fancy that clear golden wine was filling the room and his own being too. For a moment he thought that neither of them could stand it. The room was an old man's room, its walls rigid with antiquity, he himself tired to death, patched like an old kettle. They had lost the power of resilience and would crack at the seams. Then the gold slowly ebbed, drawn back into the depths of Job's singing spirit, leaving only a ripple of light on the ceiling, as though reflected from a dancing sunbeam, and a gentle warmth about the Dean's heart. Fancy, all fancy, he told himself, like the fancy that the scent of spring had come into the room with Bella and the green parrot.

"Shall I wind the clock, sir?"

"Much obliged," said the Dean, thankful to sit back in his chair and adjust himself quietly to this new Job.

How did the young effect these sudden changes? Did they, in one of those deep dreamless sleeps of youth, lying cheek on hand graceful and enchanted as though Oberon had touched them, know a metamorphosis such as Bottom knew? Or was it just what they ate? Undoubtedly Ruth fed Job well. In just a few weeks he had grown and filled out astonishingly. There was colour in his face and the hollows in his cheeks and the dark lines under the eyes had vanished. His hair, cut shorter, grew now with a strong wiry twist, full of vitality. He held his shoulders straight and his head well up, as though he respected himself and his work. He had changed from boy to young man. His hands on the clock were deft and sure and whilst he was attending to it he took no notice of the Dean. He had forgotten him. The Dean too was respectfully silent. One did not disturb an artist at his work or a saint at his prayers.

Job finished his work and shut the bag. Then he turned back to the Dean, his eyes sparkling with excitement. "Sir! I'm reading Mr. Penny's books."

"I thought you would," said the Dean. "What do you read?"

"Just what I pick up off the floor, sir. Plato. Shakespeare. Charles Lamb. Wordsworth. It's all grand stuff, even when I don't understand it. Mr. Penny helps me. Polly never learnt to read properly at Dobson's, like I did, so Miss Peabody lets me go up one evening a week after supper and we sit in front of the fire and I teach her."

He had come back to the Dean's table and the words poured out as he told him of his affairs. Adam Ayscough had thought him changed from boy to man, but now he was back in some childhood he had never had, telling a grown-up he loved and trusted the glorious tale of his accomplishments without the slightest doubt that the other would be as thrilled as he was. The Dean could not remember that such a thing had happened to him before. He listened with one hand behind his ear, fearful lest he should miss a word of it.

Job suddenly caught himself up, aware of some slight sound outside the door, as of a prowling presence there. He flushed scarlet. "Please forgive me, sir. I should have gone away when I had wound the clock. That's what Mr. Garland told me to do."

"Had you done so, Job, you would have deprived me of a very great happiness. I am more obliged to you than you can well know. Before you go tell me of Mr. Peabody. I understand he is indisposed? Is it his asthma?"

"No, sir, only a cold. He's well over his asthma."

"Had he had asthma previously?"

"Yes, sir. It was only to be expected, Polly said."

"The weather has been very inclement."

"It wasn't the weather, sir, it was you."

"Me?" asked the Dean, his hand behind his ear again.

"Being ill, sir. Mr. Peabody always has asthma when he is miserable."

76

The Dean did not like to ask Job to repeat himself, but he believed he had heard aright. Bella. Job. Isaac. It appeared that they all felt affection for him. He struggled for speech and when it came at last its banality shocked him.

"My compliments to Mr. Peabody. You will tell him, if you please, that during my illness I have been continuing my study of horology. To the books he lent me I have added others from the library." He moved the sheets of manuscript and architectural plans that were piled on his table and showed Job the books that lay under them, calf-bound histories of clocks and clock-makers. "Tell Mr. Peabody I am his humble pupil and I shall hope soon to visit you both at the shop to choose the clock for my wife. My compliments to Miss Peabody, Mr. Penny, Polly and Ruth. I hold you all in my heart. There is Garland at the door. Good-bye, Job. Much obliged."

ANDRÉ'S POEMS

RANULPH, standing in front of the fire, his hands in his pockets, watched him. In spite of the dim light he could see André's face go dead white and see how his hands trembled. He turned his back on him and lit the candles on the mantelpiece. When he turned round again it was to find André fixing him with eyes blazing with anger. The mixture of emotions in his face, fury and bewilderment with joy struggling somewhere behind them, was so comic that Ranulph laughed. The laugh added fuel to André's rage.

"Did you—dare—to take my papers from my desk and read them?" he stuttered.

Ranulph laughed again. "Come, come, man, it didn't take all that courage. You're not as formidable as all that."

André scented contempt, and flushed hotly. "It was unpardonable," he said.

"Oh, quite," said Ranulph drily, "most of the things I do are. It was your own fault though. You let me loose on the farm on

77

Christmas morning. I naturally ransacked your room. What else would you expect?"

André choked and Ranulph went gaily on. "Having found what I considered works of genius I naturally sent an example of them to an expert for his opinion. I always refer everything to experts. It saves trouble in the end. I was flattered to find his opinion coincides with my own." He flicked the letter in André's hands with his finger, and André looked down again at the sentences that seemed burning themselves into his brain . . ."miracles of loveliness. Both poems and essays have a luminous beauty that is most arresting . . . The power of deep thinking linked with both beauty and simplicity of expression is rare . . . It is difficult to launch an unknown poet, but nevertheless at whatever risk to myself this one must be launched . . . I hope you will be able to send me the rest of his work to consider . . . I shall congratulate myself upon having the opportunity . . . I shall be happy to meet—"

Ranulph's voice cut across the butter-smooth sentences. "One more bit of evidence for the superiority of my judgment over other people's—yours for instance. I gather since you apparently did nothing with them, that you thought nothing of your own work?"

André moistened his dry lips with his tongue. An intense palpitating joy was slowly creeping in and eating up his anger.

"I sent it to one or two publishers; they thought nothing of it," he said hoarsely.

"And you sat down under their opinion? You aided and abetted them in hiding your light under a bushel? How like you! How like your crawling subservient humility!"

Again there was a tiny lash of contempt in Ranulph's voice. André's anger flickered back again at its touch.

"You have, I believe, done me an immeasurable service . . . But yet you had no right—"

"Not at all," said Ranulph easily, "my behaviour was quite unprincipled, but then, lucky for you, I have no principles . . . Sometimes, André, I wonder what measure of success would ever come to the children of light if they had not got the children of this world to boost them." He smiled and filled his pipe. "Yes, that's it. Every successful child of light is surrounded by a little group of worldly children who take the bushel off the flame, shout about its brilliance, tell lies about its heat, blow out, when possible, rival flames, haggle for terms and generally advertise heaven by the methods of hell."

He laughed and André, trembling, groped for the chair beside the fire. "Yes, André, there's money to be made out of you, and Blenkinsop, aided by me, will make it. Trust Blenkinsop. That's all bunkum about the difficulty of launching unknown poets. Blenkinsop wouldn't be gurgling about the cost to himself of publishing your work unless he thought it was a loss likely to be repaid a thousandfold. Yes, André, you're rare. Didn't you know you were rare?"

He spoke suddenly very gently, drew up a chair opposite to André and sat down, looking at him.

"No." André, looking up, saw the queer tawny eyes, alight and eager, fixed on him. It struck him, irrelevantly, that in their eagerness and colour they were like Peronelle's. But he was too stunned to follow out the idea. Ranulph leant back in his chair, and began to talk, quietly and appreciatively and with deep insight, of André's work. He seemed not to have forgotten a single word of the poems and essays he had read. He quoted whole lines of them and all the thought in them he seemed to make his own. As he talked André felt all anger melt out of him, its place taken by a sensitive shrinking . . . Those poems had been self-revealing and now this man, a stranger whom he disliked, had, in reading what he had written, read him too. Ranulph talked on and gradually this sensitiveness receded. So great was the man's understanding that he felt something of the relief of a penitent who has shared the burden of self-knowledge with his confessor, followed in its turn by almost a feeling of affection for this man who knew his secrets. Then all other feeling was swamped in a flood of joy, a joy that as yet he could not quite analyse. He felt liberated. He felt, in anticipation, fulfilled. He felt alive and growing. Skilfully Ranulph turned the talk from André's writing to himself. He spoke with admiration of André's toil and with sympathy of his frustration. Letting loose his story-teller's gifts he built a rosy picture of André's future as a writer. Warming to his subject he leaned forward in his chair, waving his pipe and gesticulating... André was reminded suddenly of an elder brother telling him stories in the garden at Le Paradis... He began to smile at the other's vehemence.

"And what of the farm?" he asked.

"You must get a good bailiff. You must waste no more time over the farm. It is a criminal, damnable shame that your talents should be wasted ... Waste ... There's nothing worse in this world and nothing more tragic than the right man in the wrong place. Stay on at Bon Repos by all means, it's your home and you and Rachell have created its spirit, but waste no more time on pig-wash. Get a good bailiff."

"And how am I to pay him?" smiled André. "If, as you think, a writer's career is before me it will yet be some time before my earning powers can support bailiffs."

"Get a bailiff with money of his own who will throw in his lot with yours and leave you his money when he dies," said Ranulph.

André laughed out loud.

"This is not midsummer eve," he said. "I shall not find such a rare bird under a rose bush at midnight."

"It is Good Friday and you will find him on the other side of the hearth," said Ranulph.

André stared and the laughter went out of his face. "You?"

"Yes," said Ranulph, "I. I've been a wanderer all my life and I'd like to anchor at Bon Repos. I love the place, every stick and stone of it. I ask nothing better than to stay here. I'm a good farmer—I've given you proof of that—and I have money—plenty of it. I'll put it into the farm. If I die first all that I have will be yours."

André did not answer. Ranulph saw that all joy, amusement, gratitude and affection were draining away from his face, leaving it like a stone. He realized bitterly that hidden under all surface emotions André had a fundamental dislike of him ... He did not want him at Bon Repos.

"I could not let you do that," said André harshly.

"Why not?"

"It's fantastic and I should not wish to give up all control of my own farm."

"It would not be necessary for you to do that, or to give up all the work even. A little practical work is necessary to thought, I know—the rhythm of it. We would work together, but you would be free of all anxiety, able to come and go as you wished."

"I could not possibly accept all that service from a stranger. It is strange to me that you should offer it . . . What makes you?"

"Love of Bon Repos."

"You talk more like a crazy idealist than like the practical man of affairs that you are. You know as well as I do that these compacts between strangers end badly."

"I am no stranger." He spoke seriously and André feared that he had wounded him.

"No," he said generously, "you have been and are an amazingly good friend. I have no words to thank you. But there is no tie of blood between us —"

"Yes." The word seemed to rip across the quietness of the room as though a curtain were torn from top to bottom. André looked up startled, and found the other man's eyes fixed on him piercingly. He felt, as Rachell had felt, that Ranulph had come right in to him, had taken possession of him. He felt almost a little thrill of fear and was aware again of the far away moaning of the wind, coming like a traveller from far distances, beating with its clamour about Bon Repos, sweeping on again into invisible space. This man in front of him, he felt, had something of the quality of a storm about him, something mysterious and restless, fierce and clamorous. He had felt this power often in the sailors and Island born men whom he had known—this strength of the sea, and surge of the tides active in a man's blood. He leant forward, gazing at Ranulph, afraid, yet drawn irresistibly to him.

Ranulph smiled. "André, to think that you wrote those amazing poems and then thought so little of them that you knuckled under to the opinion of two beggarly publishers! And to hide them away even from Rachell. What an instance of your appalling self-depreciation! Even as a baby you were like that—the result of our father's bullying. We were both driven to loneliness by it, both of us. I rebelled and went off by myself, you hid . . . Well, we've come together again now."

A CAROL SERVICE

EIGHT o'clock struck, the deep notes of it falling down and down from the heights of the starry sky to this deep vault where they were sitting. Then there was an utter silence, not a sound from the waiting congregation, not even the rustle of a turning page or the breath of a sigh, nothing but a deep silence in which, surely, the happy ghosts were gathering thickly in the shadows. Henrietta could picture them; the cowled monks who had served the monastery, the townspeople who had made the city of Torminster, all the men and women and little children who had lived out their lives in the shelter of the great Cathedral and welcomed Christmas year after year, generation after generation, in this very place; and Nicolas de Malden himself, clad in his dark brown habit, girt about the waist with rope, not gaunt and dying as when he had painted the chapel walls, but happy and enthralled as she had so often seen him working at his missal.

The silence was broken by a thin thread of music. Far away in the nave the choir were singing.

> *Oh little town of Bethlehem,*
> *How still we see thee lie!*
> *Above thy deep and dreamless sleep*
> *The silent stars go by.*
> *Yet in thy dark streets shineth*
> *The everlasting light;*
> *The hopes and fears of all the years*
> *Are met in thee tonight.*

Their voices swelled and grew louder, for they had reached the entrance to the crypt and were coming slowly down the worn steps; so worn by countless worshippers that they were bent to the shape of a bow as though always weighed down by the feet of the multitude.

Oh morning stars together
Proclaim the holy birth,
And praises sing to God the King,
And peace to men on earth;
For Christ is born of Mary;
And, gathered all above,
While mortals sleep, the angels keep
Their watch of wondering love.

The congregation could sing too now, as the crossbearer came into sight with behind him the choir in their red festival cassocks, and then Peppercorn leading the clergy.

How silently, how silently,
The wondrous gift is given!
So God imparts to human hearts
The blessings of his heaven.
No ear may hear his coming;
But in this world of sin,
Where meek souls will receive him, still
The dear Christ enters in.

The clergy were all in the chapel now, and Henrietta could see their faces through the open door. It was funny and yet it was touching. Shock, incredulity, bewilderment and wonder took possession of their faces one by one, to be followed at last by that look of adoration and peace that had been on Grandfather's face from the beginning; that peace which only the experience of perfection can give to a human soul. The Dean, a gentleman of uncertain temper, looked as peaceful as any. They need not have feared him.

They sang all the familiar carols one by one in the echoing darkness, and then the Dean, standing in the chapel door, blessed them, and the clergy and choir went away as they had come, singing up the steps and down the nave, their voices dying away into a thread of sound and then to silence. Then the congregation came to life and began to move towards the chapel for their annual sight of those superb painted walls. Grandmother, Ferranti and Hugh Anthony went with them, eager to hear what they said when they saw the missal-like Christmas tree, the Baby and the shepherds.

But Nicolas and Henrietta flew up the steps to the deserted nave above, overwhelmed by the terror which seizes all creators when their creation is exposed for the first time to the gaze of man . . . The first Creator felt it, surely, when Adam's eyes opened upon the garden which he had made . . . But it was a happy terror and they laughed as they held hands in the darkness; for they had looked upon what they had made and they knew that it was very good.

Nine o'clock struck and, as always at the conclusion of a carol service, the Christmas bells began to ring.

WINKLE IN THE BROOM CUPBOARD

I N the passage Winkle by-passed the lavatory and went into the broom cupboard next door. There was a housemaid's box on the floor, and she sat down upon it with much satisfaction. She had a naturally cheerful disposition and could be happy anywhere, but in school hours she was happiest inside the weeping willow on Mrs. Belling's lawn or inside the broom cupboard. It was the peace and privacy that she liked in these retreats. No one bothered her, and she could escape to her country without fear of being seized and dragged back again before she had even had time to knock on the door. Sitting with her fat hands folded in her lap, she looked with affection at the white-washed wall opposite her, and wished the sun would move upon it in the way she liked. But it was grey today. She turned towards the small square high window and saw it framing the branch of a plum-tree with its blossom white against the grey sky. A ringdove alighted on the branch and swung there. She sighed with contentment and her eyes did not leave the flowering branch and the blue-grey wonder of the bird.

"Please," she said softly, "could I go there now?"

She had a moment of anxiety, wondering if she would be able to

84

go. When she had been very small she had never wondered, the mere flash of a bird's wing, a snow-flake looking in at the window or the scent of a flower had been enough to send her back. Lying in her cot, rolling about on a rug on the lawn, sitting in her high chair eating her bread and milk, she had gone back with ease to that other place. And she had not exactly gone back, she had been lifted back by the small lovely sights and sounds and scents, as though it were easier for her to be there than here. But now she was five years old it was easier to be here than there. She could not go back without first secluding herself in some hiding-place such as the apple-tree at home, the rosemary-tree in the manor-house garden or the willow-tree here, without climbing the steps to the door with the least suspicion of an effort, and that little pang of anxiety lest today she might not be able to make the effort. And always at the back of her mind nowadays there was the fear that the day might come when not only would she be unable to make the effort, but that she would not want to go back. Even now, at home, she did not find herself wanting to go back very often, because it was nice at home. It was here at school that the longing to go back came upon her so overwhelmingly, though not so overwhelmingly as it used to do. Perhaps one day she would have forgotten that she had ever gone back. Nothing would remain of her returns to the other place but a vague longing.

But that time was a long way off yet, and meanwhile with relief and unspeakable joy she found herself making the effort and climbing the steps. They were silvery steps and might have been made of light, and they led to the low small door in the rock that had a knocker on it, just like the knocker on the door of the dolls' house where Hunca Munca and Tom Thumb had such adventures in the *Tale of Two Bad Mice*. When Winkle knocked with the knocker, the door was opened from the inside. A year ago the door had opened at once, but now she sometimes had to wait a little, and just occasionally felt worried lest this time it should not open. A year ago she had been small enough to pass through the door without bending her head, but now she had to stoop. If she got much bigger even stooping would not get her through, for it was an exceedingly small door.

She knocked, waited a moment, the door opened and she stepped through into the branch of swaying blossom. Beside her was the dove, and they swung there together in the still grey peace.

"Coo-*coo*, coo-coo," said the dove. Winkle never knew quite what it would be that cradled her. It might be golden praise or the blue of purity or scarlet courage, or just light, or just darkness. It depended on the day and the time. They were all good, but the light was very good because it enabled her to see right to the horizons of the country where the mountains were. The darkness was best of all, even though she saw nothing and did nothing in it, because it loved her.

Nowadays she always enjoyed the nearest things first because they were the most familiar, bearing some likeness to the things she had left behind. As she passed on, things became more glorious and less familiar. Once, she half remembered, it had been the other way on. The things that bore some likeness to the things of this world had been less familiar than what was beyond, and she had passed through them very quickly in her haste to get home.

Yet though there was a likeness in the silvery whiteness of the flowers about her to the blossoms on Mrs. Belling's plum-tree, that bloomed before the apple-tree at home had even stuck out its first green spikes of leaves, they were different here from there. They were beautiful there, but here they were not just beautiful but beauty. They were so light that they were a foam of whiteness like moonbeams about her, and yet she could lie back on them, and they held her so gently that she felt nothing but the gentleness and yet so strongly that she never felt so safe. The whiteness was not just something that was clean for the moment, like a newly washed pinafore that trembled for itself, but something that sparkled with a purity that was fearless because it was for ever. The gentleness was not only gentleness but an absence of all violence for always. The strength was not just strength but no possibility of weakness or failure. Everything here was like that. It was two things, and the second thing was always something that made the first thing immortal with its own immortality.

With invisible sweet airs rocking the fragrance and the light that

86

held her, Winkle gazed at the miracle of a plum blossom that swung above her. It seemed to her the same size as she was, and so she could see its perfection in a way that she could not do in the world on the other side of the door. But perhaps it was not quite true to say it was the same size as she was, because size did not exist here. It was simply that here she and a flower and a dove were on a complete equality. She could not, here, have trodden on a plum blossom and crushed it. The dove beside her could not have pecked her and hurt her. That sort of thing did not happen here. But the remembrance that she had once trodden on a flower made Winkle look at the blossom with a humble adoration that was the same as being on her knees. Indeed, she thought she was kneeling as she looked at the flower face to face. The six white petals were like the sails of a small ship, exactly the size for a child to sail away in upon the sea of peace. They were exquisitely shaped, beautifully shadowed, and veined with light, and a fragrance drifted from them that was the scent of the grey peace. The group of long silvery stamens tipped with gold, rising from the delicate green heart of the flower, were like an angel's crown. She could look deep into the heart, down into a green cavern of refreshment. It was like drinking cold water when you are thirsty. Beyond the flowers light shone through the silk curtains of the green leaves, and beyond them was depth beyond depth of peace. It held Winkle, and held the dove too as she leaned back against its warm breast.

She turned her head so that her cheek was against its feathers. She knew it would not fly away. Here, nothing you loved ever flew away. She could stay here for a hundred years if she liked, nestled up against the dove. One didn't talk about years here, any more than one talked about size, because there wasn't any time, but the language of the world into which she had been born five years ago was beginning to be a part of her now, and was becoming the language of her thought. Once it had not been so. Once she had known a far more wonderful language than the earthly one, but she had forgotten it now, and heard only vague echoes of it in the song of the birds and the sound of the wind blowing. Out in the world she grieved sometimes because she had forgotten it and could not talk about the things that that language only could express; but perhaps no one would have listened to her if she had, because there she was only a child. Here there was no question of being one age or another, young or old, and she had had great wisdom here once, and she believed that she had it still, only the more worldly wisdom she acquired there the less she seemed able to remember this country's wisdom. There, she was sorry about that too sometimes, but here she knew it did not matter. When her life out there was over she would come back here again, like a tired bird returning full circle to its nest. All that she seemed to lose she would find again; only she would be even richer than she had been, because she would bring back with her the gathered treasure of her flight to add to the treasure of this heavenly country. But she wouldn't keep it, for one kept nothing here. One gave it, as the flowers were giving their scent and the dove her warm breast. There was equality here. To give everything was, in this place, the meaning of equality.

She looked down at the dove's soft feathers and stroked them. When she looked closely at them she saw they were not grey at all but iridescent with colour. It seemed you could not have peace without the other colours too, the praise and joy and courage and all the other lovely tints. They all went to the making of it, and so it was lovelier even than they were. And the light was better still. And the darkness best of all.

"Dear night," she whispered, and shut her eyes and wriggled closer to the dove. The dove's eyes, too, she knew, were hooded now, and the petals of the flower were closed. The three of them were equal as the darkness held them. But presently the dove would wake and stir, and she would wake too, and the petals would open and make themselves into a boat for her, and she would sail away over the grey sea to the far horizons where the mountains were. She had never been to the mountains, but she had always known that she would go. Perhaps it would be today. Soon. Now.

A BLUE BIRD IN THE GARDEN

THE blackbird in the ilex-tree started his evening song and from the wild garden came the voices of the children calling to each other in a last game before bed.

Then suddenly they came tearing helter-skelter through the gate behind the guelder-rose bush, across the lawn and in through the garden door into the drawing-room. Ben dashed in first and went straight to David, that shadow that had once been between them entirely forgotten.

"We saw a blue bird in the garden!" he shouted. "We saw a blue bird!"

"We *did*!" yelled Tommy belligerently, though no one had contradicted him. "Not a kingfisher but bright blue like forget-me-nots."

And Caroline, sucking her thumb, nodded vigorously.

David, the children at his heels, went out to investigate, but there was nothing to be seen in the wild garden excepting the darting leaf-like bodies of the tits and the thrush singing in Methuselah; and presently Ellen came out to haul the children off to bed. "A blue bird!" she scoffed. "Moonshine!"

"It was *not*!" said the children indignantly.

"I believe you," David assured them, and they went off comforted.

He lingered in the wild garden. It was incredibly beautiful with that silvery mist of traveller's joy everywhere about him, the purple shadows gathering under the trees and a few golden leaves drifting down silently out of the golden sky. He began to feel almost happy. It was so long since he had felt happy that the strangeness of the sensation was quite startling. "Traveller's joy." That was what he was feeling; the joy of the traveller who returns to his own place. That was what Aramante had felt when she came back to her own spot of earth and her soul flew back to her breast like a homing bird.

And with happiness there came to him also a new sense of creative power. The fact that he had been able to do what he had done, to love so deeply and yet to relinquish his love, had increased his faith in himself. He looked back with shame to the mood of defeatism at the Hard, when he had thought that the days that are past are better than these days. That was all nonsense. Life was what one made it. As those who had lived before him in this place had built finely, so would he. He remembered a verse in Ecclesiasticus that Lucilla had often quoted to him. "And say not thou that former years were better than those of the present time; for that is the talk of a foolish person."

Suddenly from oak-tree to lilac bush there was a brilliant flash of blue. Not a kingfisher, as Tommy had said; a paler and more ethereal blue than that. In two strides David was at the lilac bush and had taken in his hands old Mary's blue budgerigar. Incredibly, by some miracle, it had survived rain and storm and the hatred of other birds. Perhaps it had been caught by someone and escaped again . . . Perhaps, he smiled to himself, it was a fairy bird and could not die . . . Holding the soft fluttering feathers in his cupped hands David thought that he must return her bird to old Mary; but then he remembered that Hilary had said in a letter that he had given Mary a new budgerigar, a green one, and that she was comforted. He would let the creature go. Undoubtedly it was a fairy bird, or it could not have survived.

He lifted his hands and opened them. The bird spread its wings and flew up and up above the tree-tops into the golden sky. David watched as long as he could but suddenly the light dazzled him and he shut his eyes. When he opened them again the bird had gone; earth-bound, with eyes that could not stand the glory of light, he had lost sight of it; yet through the little incident the conviction that he had longed for suddenly came to him. "It's true," he thought. "The spirit of man *has* wings."

A DISCOVERY

Entirely unaware that in revealing David to Old Beaver as being made of the same stuff as himself he had precipitated a crisis, Ben conducted his elders to the store-room. "There!" he said. "Illustration from some child's picturebook, my foot!"

Pausing to pull up the knees of his trousers, and nearly driving Ben mad by this sartorial caution, David folded himself up beneath the shelf to examine the phenomenon beneath it. John Adair, who suffered from rheumatism in his knees, waited for his verdict before deliberately courting unnecessary suffering.

"Might be worth investigating, I think," said David.

The coolness of the report infuriated Ben.

"*Might be!* Can't you see the rabbit?"

"Well, yes. Now you mention it there's something here that might be a rabbit."

John Adair sighed, and with loudly cracking joints crawled beneath the shelf. His reaction was far more satisfactory than David's. After a few muttered exclamations he exploded into sudden enthusiasm.

"By my beard, I believe the boy is right! But the darned shelf is in the way. Get the tool-box, Ben. Look lively!"

Ben dashed off for the tool-box, returning with it to find both men with their coats off clearing the shelf of Nadine's jams and chutneys. For three hours they worked feverishly. They took all the bottles down to the kitchen, unfortunately breaking a few in the process, and removed the shelves from the wall; groaning as they got out the nails that had pierced right through the wallpaper to whatever was beneath it. "Sacrilege!" ejaculated John Adair. "Bloody sacrilege!" Then they set to work to remove what they could of the distemper and paper. It was easier than they had expected. The little room was damp, the distemper was already peeling off and the two layers of paper came away in solid strips.

Beneath them damp stains and patches of paste spread a dingy film over what was below; but there was no doubt about it that what was below was buried treasure.

"Let it alone!" John Adair shouted at Ben, who was trying to peel off a patch of paste with his fingers. "Don't touch it, you young vandal! This filth must be got off with the proper stuff, if you don't want to harm the fresco. That's all we can do for now; but, by gad, we've done a good day's work. Look at it, you chaps. Look at it! Sixteenth century at a rough guess. Floor to ceiling the whole way round. Look at that bit of colour there—the blue and the green. When we get that cleaned it will be as fresh as the day it was painted. I should say it's a wood or a garden. Now praised be God who has matched me with this hour."

"Is that shape there a chap on a horse?" asked David. "Gosh, what a find!"

"And look there!" cried Ben. "There's a cross there!"

"Bless the boy! Where?"

"There! On the east wall. That's where the altar would have been. This *was* a chapel."

They sat down on a pile of shelves, got their breath and stared incredulously. Until they could get the walls properly cleaned they would not know the full glory of their find; but that there was glory there they knew. They were like men staring at the shifting mists obscuring a heavenly landscape, seeing through it no more than shreds of colour, hints of celestial shape, yet aware the longer they looked that to see the whole was worth any price whatever that could be paid.

"And God knows there's enough here already," said John Adair gently. "Enough, in all conscience, to make a man glad he lived to see it."

"The more you look the more you see," said David. "Surely that's a man on a horse. A white horse, I think—or will be when he's clean. Dogs round him, perhaps? And I should say he's a dressy fellow. That red and blue is where his coat would be."

Ben gave a sudden shout.

"It's the white deer! The one in the alcove! The white deer holding up the cross in his antlers!"

"Where?" demanded David.

"There! Behind the altar!"

"The wish is father to the thought," murmured John Adair.

"No, sir. Look there. You can see his neck, his pointy face. He's turned his head to look at the man, and the man has reined in his horse to look at the deer. The horse was galloping a minute ago. Look at his legs. He's been halted suddenly, and his hoofs are slipping on the wet grass of the wood. The animals and the birds, they're just going about their business in the wood, not taking any notice. No, look at that old dog! He's bowed his head. He's worshipping. So's the man, I think, though his head's high. No, he's not looking at the deer; he's looking at the cross."

His elders, looking intently, could make out little of all this.

"Since you say so," murmured John Adair. "I've not my glasses."

"I think he's right," said David slowly.

"I don't doubt it. His long-distance vision is extremely good." From somewhere far away in the house there came a faint hail. "I suppose we now let the family in on this?"

"No!" said Ben sharply.

He couldn't bear the thought of everybody knowing about this place. If Father or Mother, or Malony, or someone, were to call the walls a dirty mess he would murder them.

"No help for it," said David. "What's your mother going to say when she comes home and finds jam-pots all over the kitchen floor?"

"Oh, gosh, if it just didn't happen to be a store-room!" groaned Ben.

David got up quietly and went out of the room. The hail had been George's, but he thought he had heard Sally's voice too. He ran down the turret stairs and went through the kitchen to the hall . . .

"We've something to show you," he said quickly. "We've found something—your father and Ben and I. Come along and see it. You, too, Uncle George. Glad it's you and Sally to see it first."

George heaved himself to his feet. David put his hand into Sally's arm and hurried her along. She came laughing. She did not

93

quite know what had happened; except that David was suddenly nearer than he had ever been, and that the whole world shone with clear light. They ran up the turret stairs, George lumbering after.

"There!" said David, at the store-room door, and took his hand from her arm.

While the others gazed not at the frescoes but at her, she stood in the centre of the little room unaware of them, still pink-cheeked and bright-eyed, still unconsciously holding the armful of spindle-berries, and gazed about her with adoring wonder; not amazed exactly, because that supreme joy of childhood, the expectation of gloriously unlikely things likely to happen at any moment, was still hers, but yet at the same time deliciously surprised to find the expected unlikeliness quite so unlikely as all this.

"There's the Chevalier on his horse, riding through Knyght-wood," she said. "It's rather like the picture I told you about, David—the one I saw somewhere, but couldn't remember. I used to see the wood behind Ben, and then I saw it behind you, that day in Knyghtwood. You were looking at a kingfisher. What's he looking at? Could it be the twins' Fairy Person with the Horns?"

The voice of George made itself heard.

"What on earth are you talking about, Sally, and what the dickens is Nadine going to say to all this mess?"

"All this mess, General, is, I believe, a most priceless sixteenth-century fresco," said John Adair, still sitting upon the pile of shelves, and now smoking a pipe to calm himself. "Of course we'll need to get the thing cleaned up before we can be certain about it, but I shall be very much surprised to find myself mistaken."

A WET DAY

MEG, wearing mackintosh boots and a red mackintosh, and with a red sou'-wester tied beneath her chin, splashed down the drive, and under the dripping oak-trees, in a state of happiness deeper and more perfect than any other she was likely to know while she lived in this world. Had she known that she would never be happy in quite this way again she would not have been so happy, but she did not know. She was four years old, and much beloved, and regarded happiness as the normal state of everybody. She was not happy when her tummy ached or she had a cold in her head, or when her mother or father went away and left her, or when the black beast pounced; at such times the depth of her misery was quite appalling; but those awful times did not come very often, and in between were these long stretches of shining joy.

She thought it was a glorious squelchy day. The drive was in a deplorable state, full of ruts and holes, and pools of rain-water brimmed them all. Meg zig-zagged from one to the other, planting a booted foot firmly in the middle of each, so that fountains of water shot up into the air to descend again upon her head, together with rain-drops dripping from the oak-trees, in a perfect deluge of sun-shot gleaming silveriness. Every time this happened she chuckled softly, and Mouse, running at her heels, barked joyously. Mouse, a microscopic grey cairn, was two years old. She had been given to Meg by her father when Robin, Meg's brother, had been born, so that Meg as well as her mother should have a tiny thing to care for. She had a minute pointed face, very long whiskers and a small dainty head with only two ideas in it—Meg and dinner. Of these two ideas Meg was the predominant one. She loved Meg with a love that was out of all proportion to the size of her body. She went where Meg went, loved whoever and whatever Meg loved; and as Meg loved nearly everybody, she loved nearly everybody too. She had no life apart from Meg and would gladly have died for her. Because Meg liked splashing in the wet she liked it too, and because Meg gloried in this day she also thought it a gift for the two of them sent straight from heaven.

And it was a good day. The sun and the rain were flying and the whole world was washed in silver and drenched with the scents of wet earth and grass and flowers, the smell of the sea and the aromatic pungent smell of herby things that grew in the sea-marshes beyond the oak-wood. Over her head the bits of sky that Meg could see between the wet leaves were thrilling: a patch of bright blue here, a bit of inky storm-cloud there, a bit of rainbow somewhere else. The cry of the gulls was wild and high and excited, and within the walled garden there was a blackbird singing.

Meg looked ridiculous. Mackintoshes being the price they were, her splashing outfit had been bought large enough to allow for growth. The bottom of her mackintosh descended to her ankles and the sleeves to the tips of her fingers. The brim of her poppy hat, weighted with water, flapped to her nose in front and descended over her ears each side. There was nothing to be seen of her except a small pointed sunburnt chin with water-drops trickling off it, and yet a keen observer, hidden behind the oak-trees, would have known quite a lot about Meg just by watching her progress down the drive. The sheer ecstasy with which her booted feet came down in each puddle told of the depth of her capacity for happiness. And yet her chuckle was without undue excitement and devoid of squeak. It would seem she knew already, with subconscious knowledge, that restraint is estimable in women, and would love it and exercise it all her life. And she was game. It was obvious that she would not cry if she tripped over the hem of her ridiculous mackintosh and fell headlong, for not even that ungainly flapping garment could hide the trim gallantry of her little figure. She was determined, too. Though she zigzagged from puddle to puddle, she was never deflected from her determined progress down the drive. She knew where she was going and what she was going to do when she got there.

DECORATING THE CHURCH

FRONIGA pillaged her garden and the hedgerows of the lane, and then, laden with holly, ivy, Christmas roses and rosemary, she walked quickly to the church. At the churchyard gate she met Parson Hawthyn, cheerful but hobbling painfully upon his stick. "I climbed hedges like a ten-year-old yesterday," he said with a chuckle, "but this morning I know my age. Thank you, Froniga; that's a fine big Christmas posy. Is that poor woman still with you?"

96

"No," said Froniga. "When I got up this morning I found the gypsies had gone and so had she."

"Not back to her cottage?" asked Parson Hawthyn in distress.

"I'm afraid so," said Froniga. "When she saw the gypsies had gone she would have known she would be safe there. What can we do now?"

"Nothing at this moment," said Parson Hawthyn. "This is not her moment, but the children's. Look there."

She looked where he pointed and laughed, for the grey gloom of the day had parted and had let through colour and delight. A little figure in a cloak and hood of kingfisher blue, riding a white pony, was flying towards them. Just behind came a dapple grey bearing a boy in elfin green, and beside him Tom's face shone ruddy as a lantern, and his clothes, like his pony, were chestnut brown. The sound of the ponies' hoofs had been heard and more children came running out of the cottages on either side of the lane, all rosy-cheeked with pleasure and carrying holly and branches of fir, for Parson Hawthyn had summoned all his pupils to decorate the church. They were a few moments before the appointed time, but the sound of the cantering hoofs, and then the sight of Mistress Jenny riding a new pony, had brought them all flying along like a flock of birds. Froniga thought with a sudden ache of the gypsy children, and her thoughts seemed to bring them winging in from the east to join the others. Then Baw came to a standstill beside her, his head against her shoulder, his nose pushing into her hand, and Jenny slipped off his back into her arms.

Presently, when the ecstatic thank yous had been said, and all the children had patted Baw and Pal and the bolder ones had been sat on their backs and given rides, the ponies were left in Tom's care and Parson Hawthyn and Froniga led the children into the church. Both knew better than to try and use the children as their helpers; that way madness lay. They told the children what had to be done and left them free to do it as they liked, as was in any case their right upon their own festival. They themselves sat down filled with that sublime indifference to results which distinguishes the truly great after right action has been taken.

The results were good, if unusual, and if some of the holly and greenery were put in surprising places, the children did not forget the little lady and her unicorn upon the tomb. The lady had holly on her pillow and the unicorn a wreath of ivy about his neck. Parson Hawthyn had thought that the Virgin's arms could not be empty on Christmas Day, and he had carved and painted a new baby, even more beautiful than the one Cinderella had stolen. On top of a flat tomb he had made a stable with a thatched roof, and filled it with hay, and set the Virgin and Child within it, and he had carved figures of the shepherds and the animals to stand around them. The children were thrilled with this and they put the brightest bunches of holly within the stable. By common consent of the children, Jenny was left to arrange the flowers on the altar. Two of the big boys fetched her some water from the spring in the wood and with stars in her eyes she arranged the Christmas roses and rosemary, with sprigs of holly, in two pewter pots, and put them one on each side of the silver cross.

It was one of those hours in which pure joy, strong as an encircling wall, shuts out past and future as completely as intense pain can do, giving to time the quality of eternity. Neither Parson Hawthyn nor Froniga ever forgot it. The old man felt the weight of his griefs and worries fall from him. Even his body felt less heavy with age and pain. He was conscious of unseen presences within the church and warmed himself in their gaiety. He had a foretaste of paradise, and realized for the first time how full of laughter the place must be. Froniga lost herself in a dream, for to have children all about her within a wall of safety had always been the best of her dreams. Outside the bleak and drifting clouds parted for a moment and the church was filled with sunshine.

A SPRING MORNING

IT was one of those intoxicating days when all the best people go mad; and they agreed afterwards that they had, all of them, gone quite mad . . . For hawthorn petals streamed in the wind, the sun and the rain were flying, and the smell of wet red wallflowers filled the whole world . . . So how could one help it?

Eight-year-old Colin du Frocq was the first to wake that morning. He flung back his patchwork counterpane, bounded out of bed, and rushing to the window flung it wide open, shaking hundreds of wet drops off the leaves of the passion flower that clambered round it. Leaning out he looked, sniffed, and listened. The whole of him seemed vibrating to the magic of the day: his tumbled dark hair and white nightshirt ruffled by the wind, his dark eyes that shone and sparkled, his freckled nose wrinkling like a rabbit's, and his beautiful ears, shaped like a fawn's and lying very flat against his head, trembling as do the ears of all wild things whose hearing is acute . . . And certainly that day was enough to make the stolidest vibrate . . . Such a shining before the eyes of golden sunshine, sparkling raindrops all in a row upon every twig and wet leaves silver-sheeted; such scents of drenched earth, flowers, and the salt sea; such a singing of birds in the bushes and wind in the trees, clear and distinct against the muffled roar of waves breaking upon the beach below the cliff.

It was one of those days when the man with a ship sets sail for the skyline, the man with a horse mounts it and gallops towards the horizon, and the man who has dreamed a dream, no matter how crazy, gives chase that it may come true.

Colin had neither ship nor horse, but he had a pair of strong brown legs, and his head was packed with dreams . . . So many of them that it was difficult to know which one to take out and run after . . . However, the great thing on a day like this was to run; one would discover where to and what after when one was actually running.

He leaped from the window and plunged into his morning's toilet. He decided that there was no point in washing; he would so soon be dirty again that it would be sheer waste of time; but he cleaned his teeth because his toothpaste tasted good and if swallowed did quite a lot to assuage the pangs of hunger, and flattened out his rumpled hair with a comb dipped in the water jug before he dragged on his patched dark-blue knickerbockers and jersey. Then, his shoes in his hand, he crept barefoot out of his

99

little room and down the winding uncarpeted staircase of the old farmhouse. He gained the stone-floored hall and was across it in a flash and straining in something of a panic to turn the great key noiselessly in the front door; for if Mother or Father or the girls were to wake up and catch him he would be haled back to his room and washed and re-brushed, and all the precious minutes between dawn and breakfast would be wasted upon the banalities of the toilet.

But the key turned with no more than the tiniest protesting squeak, and he was out in the cobbled courtyard, blinking in the sun. This farmhouse where he lived, built not far from a rocky cliff top on an island in the English Channel, was very old, built of grey granite and roofed with weather-stained red tiles. It took up the north side of the courtyard, the other three being protected by the stables to the west and by thick old walls to the south and east that had been built in medieval times to keep out enemies. A wide doorway in the east wall, that had lost its door but was still crowned by its original immense lintel of solid stone, led into the lane and in the south wall a strong oak door led into the flower garden. These two were the only entrances to a home that must once have been as impregnable as a fortress.

Yet now, at the end of the nineteenth century, the farmhouse was called Bon Repos, and the strutting pigeons in the courtyard and the rustling leaves of the passion flower that climbed about the windows spoke of nothing but peace.

And a thousand pities, too, thought Colin. Who wanted peace? For himself he liked excitement and the clash of arms. He wished he had lived in the days when Pirates beached their boats in the Bay of the Gulls below Bon Repos, and came storming up the cliff to plunder and steal . . . Now that would have been something like . . . Terrified peasants, with their pigs, chickens, and cows, would have taken refuge inside the courtyard while Colin, Father, Mother and the girls, armed with clubs and daggers, would have stood in the wide doorway, under the huge stone lintel, and defended their home to the death. The lane outside would have run red with blood and the mound of corpses outside the door would have reached as high as the top of the hedge . . . Colin, scampering down the lane in question, sighed for the glories that were past.

Yet, what is imagination for if not to transport one to where one would be? It needed only a slight mental readjustment and a moment's pause to cut a stout stick from the hedge, and Colin was back in the great and bloody days, running dagger in hand towards the cliffs, to see if the news brought by a peasant was true and the Pirates were in sight.

The land ended in a sandy path that led to the edge of the cliff, and Colin went leaping and careering like a mad thing over the short sweet turf, and in and out between the gorse bushes that filled the air with a hot smell that was the very scent of sunshine, until the path ended at a great flat rock from which the cliff fell sheer away to the Bay of the Gulls below.

Here he stood and shouted for joy. The earth was green and the sea was blue and the great white gulls were crying and circling over his head. The wind seemed to have blown the whole surface of the world to white foam. Little white-capped waves were frisking on the sea, every hedge was a froth of hawthorn, and white clouds raced across the sky. Every now and then a silver shower came by on the wind, but so small and so swift that its passing was only an added delight to the glory of the day.

Abruptly Colin stopped shouting and remembered what he was here for. Transforming the dagger into a telescope he clapped it to one eye and raked the seas . . . Nothing . . . It was disappointing until he remembered that just round a jutting headland of rock was Breton Bay, with its fishing hamlet. The enemy had without doubt put in there first to loot the cottages, and they would be turning their attention to Bon Repos at any moment now. In a few minutes, if he listened, he would hear the rattle of oars in rowlocks and a man's voice singing the Pirates' song.

Nevertheless when he did hear them he was a bit disconcerted and suffered from a slight prickly sensation all over the surface of his body. It was a little difficult to make out if he really *was* hearing them, for the jolly song was hardly distinguishable from that other song the wind was singing in his ears, and the rattle of oars was almost lost in the breaking of waves over the rocks . . . In fact he could not make up his mind about it until a rowing boat suddenly rounded the headland and came tumbling over the top of a wave right into the Bay of the Gulls.

"Hi! You there! You'll be smashed on the rocks!"

Colin, sure-footed as some mountain animal, came scrambling down the steep dangerous cliff path in a tearing hurry, for the Pirate in the boat, a handsome fair-haired person in a blue shirt, who was carolling cheerfully at the top of his voice, was taking apparently not the slightest notice of where he was going.

"Mind! Look out!" yelled Colin, dancing up and down where the ripples came frilling in over the ribbed golden sand. "Look where you're going, you owl!"

The man, still singing, turned his head over his shoulder, winked at Colin, and steered his boat with superb skill between two weed-covered rocks into the calm water beyond.

Colin fell silent, struck dumb with admiration. This man, though a stranger to him, was nevertheless no mean sailor, and one, moreover, who seemed to understand the rocks and currents round the Island like a native . . . Colin kicked off his shoes and dashed into the sea to help beach the boat . . . It was not until the thing was done that he realized the enormity of his behaviour.

"Look at me helping you to get the boat in, and you a Pirate!" he exclaimed in annoyance.

"Why didn't you put a bullet through me when I rounded those rocks?" asked the Pirate. "Bit absent-minded, weren't you? Now your wives, children, and cattle are at my mercy!" And he made a dash for the steep path up the cliff. He was young, tall, and finely made, and he ran fast, but Colin could run yet faster and was there before him, brandishing the one-time telescope which had turned without any difficulty at all into a long slender rapier with a cruel point.

"Advance one yard farther at your peril!" he growled.

"We'll fight it out, shall we?" suggested the Pirate pleasantly. "You couldn't have a better place for a duel than this cove. Nice flat sandy surface. Private. Good, strengthening sea air. At twenty paces, shall we say? With rapiers?"

They returned to the stretch of golden sand, and the Pirate

stood proudly flexing his muscles while Colin stepped out the paces.

"To the death?" he asked.

"Oh, well," deprecated the Pirate. "It's surely a pity to be dead on a day like this. What do you say to the first one to draw blood taking the other one prisoner?"

"On guard!" said Colin briefly.

The Pirate took a pipe from his pocket, gave it a flourish that transformed it instantly into a rapier even deadlier than Colin's, gave a strange, high, excited cry, flung back his leonine head, and lunged.

Now there is only one grown-up in two thousand who has the true gift of make-believe. A good many of them, poor, well-meaning creatures, are quite prepared to go down on all fours as a tiger, or stand upright and paw the air as a polar bear, but they seem quite unable to shed their own identity. They are not a bear at all; they are only Uncle Henry trying to look like one. The air of condescension, or of embarrassment, or the silly fatuous smile they put on for the occasion, spoils the whole thing ... But one man in two thousand upon this earth is a man of faith, his belief a wizard's wand of creation that can make flowers blossom on a dung heap and awake the echo of trumpets from the dust of battle fought a thousand years ago ... And the Proud Pirate was one of that rare company; one of those fortunate ones who never grow up.

It was therefore a grand fight that was fought in the Bay of the Gulls, a swift, clean, splendid fight that only the gulls saw, and the white waves frisking on the blue sea and the white clouds scudding across the sky ... They enjoyed it thoroughly ... The waves dashed in as close as they could to watch, and the gulls, giving wild cries of encouragement, circled nearer and nearer. They had seen this fight often before, of course, for this was not the first time in the history of the Island that an Islander had defended his strip of earth against an invader, but they had never seen so splendid a pair of fighters; the tall fair-haired man who lunged with the grace of a practised fencer and the lithe, dark-haired boy who fought with the agility and dash of all valorous sons of the morning ... Yet there was no doubt as to where the Island's sympathy lay, for when an agonized cry of "Touché!" rang across the bay, and the Proud Pirate dropped on one knee on the sand, the gulls screamed in ecstasy and the laughing waves tossed their foam right up in the air in their joy.

COMPASSION

THE STRANGER AT THE GATE

FOR the second time that night Stella and Hodge raided the
larder, and this time Stella was afraid their thefts were
noticeable. Mother Sprigg was a generous housekeeper and
the inroads made for the benefit of Daniel and the cats made little
impression on the plenty of the larder, and she never seemed to
notice them. But Stella did not see that she could fail to notice this
time, with a huge wedge of pigeon pie gone, a hunk of bread and
cheese and a couple of apples. But she would abide the conse-
quences. That boy outside, right outside, more outside even than
Daniel and the cats, had got to be fed.

She went out into the yard again, carrying the loaded plate and a
jug of milk from the dairy, and crossed over to the barred door.
Here she set the food down on the cobbles and considered the
problem set before her. How was she to get the trunk of the tree
lifted out of position? It must be done somehow, for she could not
get to the front door without either climbing back up the roof to
her room, which would be impossible with both hands occupied, or
passing through the kitchen where Father and Mother Sprigg were
sitting. Her foster-parents were kind-hearted, but during these last
dangerous years the country people had had so many unpleasant
experiences with mutineers, spies, deserters and escaped prisoners
that now they gave scant encouragement to any unknown vagabond. It was the yard door or nothing, and Stella went to it with a
will, bending down and getting her back and head beneath the tree
trunk. Hodge did the same and together they heaved and strained
until there was no more strength left in them. But they did it! The
tree trunk lifted off the iron bars at last and Stella eased it to the
ground without too much noise. But she felt sick and dizzy when
she had done it, with the blood drumming in her ears and her
breath coming in painful gasps, and it was all she could do to pull
the great door open. But she did this too, and picking up the jug
and plate again made her way out into Pizzle Meadow, that

bordered the yard upon the north, and through which a cart track led to the gate opening upon the lane that ran along behind the stables and was the western boundary of Weekaborough Farm.

Pizzle Meadow, inhabited by the Weekaborough pigs, was a pleasant place, dotted here and there with old cider apple-trees, and with a stream running through it. Stella hurried along the cart track to the high padlocked gate and the thick thorn hedge, and after standing on tiptoe to put the plate and jug on top of one of the strong old stone pillars that supported the gate on either side, she climbed up it, dragging Hodge after her, and fell off the other side into the grass that bordered the lane. She did not usually fall off the gate like this, she usually climbed both up and down with the agility of a monkey, but she was still dizzy after her struggle with the tree trunk.

Strong bony hands lifted her and set her on her feet again, and for a brief moment their grip reminded her of her first memory, her mother's arms holding her so tightly, and her heart constricted with sudden pain, so that she was more breathless than ever.

"Why didn't you call?" demanded the boy. "If I'd known which direction you were coming from you could have handed me the grub through the bars. You need not have gone falling on your nose like that."

"Someone might have heard," panted Stella. "And hereabouts—since the mutiny and everything—they're scared of strangers."

The boy was still holding her, looking down at her, his hard hands gripping her arms above the elbows. "And aren't *you* scared of strangers?"

"Sometimes. But not of you, after the first minute when I thought you were Boney. I knew you were all right. Hodge told me."

For a moment he shifted his gaze from her to Hodge, standing beside her slowly swinging his tail, and they exchanged a long appreciative look, as man to man. Then he looked back at Stella again. The moon was so bright that he could see her face as though it were day. She was very flushed, the hood of her cloak had fallen back from her short tumbled boyish curls, and there were beads of perspiration on her forehead.

"You're all in a lather," he ejaculated.

"It was lifting the tree trunk and opening the gate," said Stella. "And you such a little 'un!" he murmured. He picked her up and carried her to the old oak-tree that grew near the gate and sat her down where the knotted roots made a comfortable arm-chair for a small person. Then he fetched the plate and jug from the top of the pillar, walking in a queer sort of way as though he were lop-sided, and as though the ground beneath his feet were red-hot, and sat down beside her, Hodge lying near them. But starving though he had professed himself to be he seemed in no hurry to eat. He set the food and drink at his feet and looked at them much as David must have looked at the cup of cold water that they brought him in the cave. But he had more common sense than David. His tribute of denial, though offered up with all his heart, was merely momentary, and having offered it he turned to Stella, said "Thank you," gently, and then fell upon the pigeon pie like a wolf.

Yet a well-mannered aristocratic wolf. Had Stella been older she would have gazed at this most unusual vagabond with bewildered speculation. But the world to Stella was still so full of surprise that all the ordinary happenings of life seemed as wonderful as fairy tales, and conversely fairy tales did not seem anything out of the ordinary. Everything and everybody was so surprising that something or somebody a bit extra surprising did not put her out at all. Besides, though she had never seen anyone in the least like this boy, she was completely at ease with him. She felt, for the first time in her life, a sense of likeness with another human creature, and a sense of safety; not so much physical safety as the safety of under-standing that comes between those who are two of a sort. Though she loved Father and Mother Sprigg so deeply she had never felt with them this particular feeling of safety. The gulf that yawned between her and the village children was only a crack between her and Father and Mother Sprigg, but it was there. Between her and this unknown boy it was not there. It was very odd. Turning to look at him she had the queer feeling that she was turning to look at herself . . . Yet she was quite sure that she did not look like this . . . She hoped she didn't for he was almost as much of a fright as poor old Daniel. That, she supposed pitifully, was because they were both outside people.

He was tall and his tattered shirt and torn trousers fluttered on a body so bony and thin that set up in a field he would have done very well as a bird scarer. But here the likeness to a scarecrow ended; indeed, a discerning grown-up, looking again at this boy, would have dismissed the analogy and thought instead of a tall reed shaken by the wind or a terrified unbroken colt galloping to the sea, but not of anything so static as a scarecrow. Even in comparative stillness, body, mind, and soul absorbed in pigeon pie, a sensitiveness and grace were apparent in this boy. The grace at present was clumsy but it had a thoroughbred air. The sensitiveness showed itself now in a stubborn defensiveness of expression and restless movements; set free from adversity it might have been a thing of smooth and responsible beauty. The physical contrasts were striking. The untidy dark hair fell over a broad low forehead, the skin very white where it had been shielded from the sunburn that tanned the rest of the face. The dark eyes were sombre beneath heavy dark eyebrows but the nostrils of the thin aquiline nose flared like those of a startled horse. Though the lips could set obstinately, laughter transfigured them to gentleness. His hands had broken nails and calloused palms but they were finely shaped. One could not see his feet for they were wrapped in bloody mud-caked bandages of torn rag. He finished eating and wiped his fingers delicately on the grass upon either side of him.

"Have you a handkerchief?" he asked Stella.

She fished a delicate little square of cambric out of her pocket and gave it to him and he blew his nose loudly and satisfyingly.

"That was almost worse than anything," he said.

"What was?" asked Stella.

"Blowing my nose into the air."

"Old Sol, our ploughman, never has a handkerchief and he does it beautifully, like this," said Stella, and she gave an exhibition; a serious and charming exhibition, quite without vulgarity.

"It needs practice," said the boy. "Would you mind—please— may I keep your handkerchief?"

There had been no pathos about him until now but in the shy pleading of his question it showed for a moment. Then it vanished as she nodded and smiled, and laughing he stuck the handkerchief in his pocket.

"My name is Stella Sprigg," said Stella. "What is your name?" To her, as to all children, names were tremendously important. Your Christian name, joining you to God, your surname linking you to your father. If you had both names you had your place in the world, walking safely along with a hand held upon either side. If you had neither you were in a bad way, you just fell down and did not belong anywhere, and if you only had one you only half belonged.

"Zachary," said the boy.

"Only Zachary?"

"Only Zachary."

"Just a Christian name?"

"That's all."

Stella looked at him with concern. Only God had hold of him. He was lop-sided. She had noticed it in his gait when she first saw him walking. Then she remembered that but for Father and Mother Sprigg she would have been lop-sided too, for her nameless mother had died. This memory deepened her feeling of oneness with Zachary and she put out a small hand and laid it on his knee.

"Do you know where you came from?" she asked wonderingly. The name Sprigg and the name Weekaborough were inseparably connected in her mind. She came from Weekaborough because she was a Sprigg. She was unable to visualize anyone without a surname coming from anywhere.

"From the moon," replied Zachary promptly. "Haven't you seen me up there?"

Stella dimpled delightedly. She loved moonlight, and when she had been smaller and in need of a playmate she had often wished that the man in the moon would come down and play with her.

"Zachary Moon," she said with pleasure, and felt she had got him a bit better supported upon the other side. Zachary put his hand on hers that lay on his knee, carefully and gently, as though it were a small bird. Then he turned her hand over and put their two palms together, as though they were the two halves of a shell. "I come from the moon and you're a star," he said. "Quite right, isn't it, that we should see each other first at night." Then he lifted her hand off his knee with a light gesture, as though he tossed back the captive bird to freedom. "But not right that you should be out of your bed so late."

He got up clumsily, still as though the ground were red-hot to his feet, and picked up the bowl and the plate; and he'd polished off his meal down to the last drop and the last crumb, just as Daniel and the cats did. Then he held out his free hand. "Come on, Stella. I'll help you over the gate."

He was very grown-up suddenly, and Stella felt chilled. But she got up obediently and put her hand in his, and they walked along silently, Zachary with his lop-sided gait, Stella light and airy as a fairy child. Hodge loped along behind. When they reached the tall locked gate Zachary helped the child and the dog to scramble over and then passed over the bowl and plate. "Thank you," he said, "I haven't tasted a meal like that since I left the moon. Good-bye, Star. Good-bye, Hodge."

There was a flat finality in his tone and Stella felt dreadful; like one half of a bi-valve shell being detached from the other half. "No, Zachary!" she pleaded. "No!"

Her chin only just reached the top of the gate. She propped it there, her hands laid upon the bar one on each side. Hodge thrust his head between the bars below and whined distressfully. Zachary looked from the little pointed face and the row of small finger-tips to the furry countenance below, as though memorizing them.

"No, what, Stella?"

"No, good-bye," said Stella.

His face grew sombre. Looking up at him Stella saw it with queer dark shadows on it, like the moon. He caught his breath sharply, as though he were going to say something more, but he seemed to change his mind, for his face set hard and without another look at her he turned away and was hidden by the thick thorn hedge. Stella did not call after him, for she knew that set look on a man's face. Father Sprigg looked like that when he had been telling her stories and had suddenly had enough of it, and put her down off his knee and went off to the milking. She never ran after Father Sprigg at those times for she knew by instinct that men do not want women with them all the time; they keep certain compartments of their life for them, and do not want them over-flowing into the wrong ones.

Yet as she walked slowly homeward through the meadow, Hodge beside her with his tail between his legs, she tumbled several times because she was crying. It was for Zachary she was crying. She was sure that neither the place that he had come from, when he had stepped into that moonlit magic hour that had enclosed them both, nor the place to which he was going when he left her, were good places . . . And he could have stayed here if Father Sprigg had not sent him away . . . He was like the bedraggled bird who once flew in from the outside darkness when snow was on the ground, circled about the lighted kitchen and then flew out again, and though she had cried out for pity he was gone so quickly, and the frozen dark was so immense, that there was nothing at all that she could do about it.

THE ABBÉ AT NEWGATE PRISON

THE Abbé wasted no time. The very next morning he presented himself at Newgate prison, joining the pitiful crowd of prisoners' friends watching at the felons' door. Owing to his respectable appearance he was the first to be admitted and was ushered straight away into the ante-room where the visitors were searched. He submitted to this process with cold distaste, even though in his case his clothes were not stripped from him and only his pockets were examined.

"What do you expect to find upon me?" he asked the turnkey who was dealing with him.

"Poison or a bit of rope, sir," was the answer. "You'd be surprised how smart the relatives of prisoners can be in providing them with the means of doing away with themselves. And that though they know they'll be flung into gaol themselves if anything of the sort is found on them."

The Abbé looked grimly round the dirty dark room where he

was standing. It was guarded by blunderbusses mounted on moveable carriages and the walls were hung with chains and fetters. "Hell above ground" they called this place. He knew how cruel the penal laws of England were at this time, and for what slight offences men and women were tortured and hanged. He had a pretty shrewd idea of the dreadfulness of the scene he would look on in a moment, and he knew that it would bring back all the horror of the past that he had tried to forget. Then abruptly he remembered the view from Beacon Hill on Christmas Eve, Stella in the small green parlour and the mummers coming through the garden gate in the moonlight. That too was England, and life.

He went down a stone passage to a door which a second turnkey, keeping guard beside it, unlocked and unbolted. Passing through he found himself in a long narrow passage, its walls formed of iron bars. On one side was a yard, round which the prison was built and where the prisoners were exercised, and on the other, behind a double grating, was the first of the prison wards.

It was even worse than he had thought, and it brought back the past more sharply than he had thought it would. Involuntarily he stepped back a few paces, his back against the bars that surrounded the courtyard. A wave of nausea swept over him and he did not see very clearly for a moment or two. There was a roaring in his ears, like the sea, and he felt deathly cold. Then he controlled himself, and stepped forward, just as the door opened again and the first of the crowd who had been waiting at the felons' gate surged through it, shouting to the men shut in behind the double grating, pressing against him, knocking him against the bars so that he had to cling to them to prevent himself being swept off his feet.

Breathing like a man in pain he forced himself to look steadily at the inmates of the dreadful cage. Most of them looked inhuman and many of them were only half clothed. The dirt and over-crowding, the noise and stench were horrible. Many of the men were sodden with drink, for by the proceeds of their begging they could purchase liquor in the prison. The begging had started already; they were thrusting wooden spoons on long sticks through the double grating, and their visitors, many of them almost as ragged as they were, were putting in their few pitiful pence. But only the strongest could keep the pence, for each man had to fight to keep what he was given. Many were too weak even to try, and these did not come to the grating. There were young boys among those weak ones and it was among them that the Abbé searched for Zachary, his eyes going slowly from one gaunt face to another. But he could not find Zachary, and with relief he turned away, pushed through the crowd of visitors and found again the turnkey who had let him in.

"Are these condemned men?" he asked.

"Yes, sir. Men condemned to the hulks or Botany Bay."

"For what offences?"

The turnkey shrugged. "Smuggling in rope to a prisoner, maybe. Hiding a thief or receiving stolen goods. Some minor offence."

"Have they been here long?"

"Months, sir, some of 'em, waiting for trial, and then waiting to be sent to the hulks."

"Where are the men condemned to the gallows?"

"In cells, sir. You can't see those."

"And the untried men?"

"Round the other side of the yard, sir."

The Abbé walked slowly round to the other side, noticing as he went the military sentinels posted on the roof. He imagined that the hour for exercise was near and that they would shoot if there was lawlessness. Once again he fought down his nausea. In France he had witnessed scenes more terrible than the one he had just left, but those scenes had taken place during a civil war, they had not been part of the normal life of a country at peace within its own borders. It was the organized horror of this wild beast show that shocked him as nothing in his life had shocked him yet.

He came to the other side, where was the ward of the untried men. The scene here was much the same but not quite so terrible because the men had not been here so long and many still had some hope. Yet it was bad enough, and if this was the scene Stella had seen in her dream he thanked God for her sake that dreams, remembered on waking, lose a little of their sharpness of horror or joy. Once more he pressed himself against the double bars, his anxious gaze going from face to face of the crowd who were pressing against them on the other side. But though he stayed there for what seemed to himself an interminable time he could not see Zachary. The depression of his weariness and horror engulfed him. It had all been for nothing. The boy was not here.

He was on the point of moving away when the pallid ravaged faces, the surging movement, the noise, reminded him of something . . . The sea . . . It was a sea of misery that was breaking against the bars only a few feet from him, as the waves had broken on the beach the other night, white and torn in the glare of the lightning. The dreadful sea came nearer, reared itself up, crashed over his head. He was drowning in the darkness, sucked down in that horror. Mon Dieu, was he losing consciousness? With all his strength he exerted his will, swung back again towards that from which he had swung away, clutched the bars tighter. Was he a squeamish woman, an untried boy, to be so overwhelmed by dreadful sights? He remembered the legend of the storm and the drowning boy saved from it; and vividly he remembered Stella's courage in the face of storm, her offered fear. He stayed his ground. His vision cleared and through a sudden gap in the crowd, as though a wave had toppled and parted, he saw a picture that he never afterwards forgot.

Under a grating high in the wall a wooden washtub had been set and four or five men were gathered about it attempting to wash their clothes. The water in the tub appeared filthy, the rags they were wringing out of it scarcely less so, yet the Abbé found the sight incredibly heartening; for here were a few men struggling after decency; men who were not yet wild beasts like the rest. One of them, stripped to the waist, had his back to the Abbé. He was a tall boy with dark tumbled hair and a thin brown back upon which the ribs showed starkly. He half-turned, wringing out his shirt, but before the Abbé could see his face the gap in the crowd had closed again and he was hidden. It might have been Zachary, or it might not, but the Abbé was not going to leave this hell above ground until he knew.

During the next twenty minutes he passed through one of the oddest experiences of his life. As he moved up and down before the bars, trying ceaselessly for another sight of that boy, he began to recognize some of the faces that came and went in front of him. One hulking brute of a fellow had the bluest Irish eyes he had ever seen. Another, a boy, with the face of a depraved old man, had a mouth as sensitively cut as Stella's own. A third, hunchbacked and deformed, had a pock-marked face that startled the Abbé by suddenly splitting into a grin. He noticed other eyes, other mouths, other gallant attempts at cheerfulness. Occasionally, when he slipped a coin into a wooden spoon, his eyes would meet the eyes of the poor devil who held it, and he had the sensation that the trivial act was not trivial at all but an actual entering in of himself into the being of the man before him. He was recognizing as though these men were not strangers and giving as though to his friends. When the appalling sea had broken over his head he had as it were passed through the breakers into the calmer water beyond. But he was in the sea now, part of it, no longer an isolated spectator on the shore. With a sudden sensation of sheer panic he knew he would never get back to the shore. Then came the calm knowledge that he did not want to. And all through the twenty minutes he was praying as he had never prayed before, every atom of himself poured out like water for those men behind the bars, but especially for one of them.

Quite suddenly he saw him again. He had finished his bit of washing and hung it on a nail to dry, and now he was leaning against the wall, shivering without his shirt. He was Zachary, but so changed that for a full moment the Abbé was not quite certain. Then, in this haggard young man leaning against the wall, his eyes dull and sombre with his hopelessness, ugly lines of exhaustion scored heavily on his face, he recognized some lingering remnants of the beauty that had so touched him in the King's child. Some of the colt-like grace was there, the mouth was the same, and the nostrils of the aquiline nose still flared like those of a startled thoroughbred. But Zachary, if like the young man in the legend he had travelled forth into the world to gain knowledge, had certainly gained it; too quickly and too much.

He was not looking at the Abbé and the turnkeys were coming down the passage, shouting that the visiting hour was over. The

Abbé called "Zachary!" but his voice did not carry to where the boy stood, and then the turnkeys were among them, seizing the visitors by the shoulders and pulling them roughly away from the bars. The Abbé in his desperation remembered their meeting in his sitting-room after the wrestling match, and how quick had been their response one to the other. Nothing that had happened since had had any power to destroy the instant liking that had been like a bridge between them. It must still hold. He did not shout again but with his eyes on Zachary he set himself to cross it. It was not difficult, for in the last twenty minutes he had issued forth from the citadel of himself as never before. Zachary turned his head and their eyes met just as a turnkey's hand descended on the Abbé's shoulder and he was pulled from the bars. It did not matter. Almost unbelieving joy shone over Zachary's face, and from the Abbé's came that gleam of light, like a rapier flashing in the sun, that had so startled Zachary at their first meeting. The Abbé, pushed backwards like the rest, a turnkey's stave against his chest, could see tears pouring down the boy's face, but only the tears of a child awaking suddenly from nightmare.

Zachary knew now that he was not forgotten in the pit into which he had fallen . . . The Abbé waved his hat, turned, and made his way back into the outer world.

PARSON HAWTHYN'S HUMANITY

"I CAME here to get water for a potion and I have nothing to carry it in," she said. "May I borrow your bottle?"

"Allow me to fill it for you, Mistress Froniga," he said courteously, and bent over the spring. He had known her for years and called her by her Christian name, yet she did not know if he liked her. She suspected that he disapproved of her. As a rule she was indifferent to the opinions of others, but today, after what he had so lately done for her, she felt less indifferent than usual. She got up, and when he had filled the bottle and the pitcher it was his turn to stand and look up into her face, so short was he. He turned his head sideways in a sparrow-like manner and said gravely, "You have been much in my thoughts today."

"Why was that?"

"I do not know," he said. "You, I expect, do know. Your knowledge is great."

"And such as you do not approve," she said, to test him.

"Froniga, disapproval is one of those things which I've thrown overboard. One does, you know, lighten the ship in old age. My dear, I shall carry this bottle of water home for you."

"Then let me lighten the ship by carrying the pitcher," said Froniga. "We will go back by way of the parsonage and leave it there."

He accepted gratefully, for he suffered from shortness of breath and carrying his water did not agree with him. The false pride that will not be helped was another thing he had shed with old age. They walked slowly along the path together and Froniga said, "But there must be many things of which as a parson you should disapprove. Sin, for instance."

"I don't disapprove of my sin," he said. "I detest it. Disapproval is far too emasculate an emotion with which to confront sin."

"Witchcraft, then," said Froniga.

"That's sin," said Parson Hawthyn uncompromisingly.

"White witchcraft?" asked Froniga.

"Froniga, I lack knowledge of the art, and I speak under correction, but I should say—when practised by a silly woman, rubbish, when practised by a wise one, dangerous unless she possesses the virtue of humility in marked degree."

"In that case she might not be able to instil faith and confidence in the sick," said Froniga shortly.

"I have always felt that that might be her difficulty," said Parson Hawthyn, and looked up at her with such merriment at having scored a point that she laughed and changed the subject.

"This path is no place for argument," she said. "I am always happy on this path. Are you?"

"I am happy anywhere," said the old man simply.

"You were not happy at Will's breeching," Froniga chided him.

"The sun is still there, Froniga, even if clouds drift over it.

Once you have experienced the reality of sunshine you may weep, but you will never feel ice about your heart again."

Ice about your heart, squeezing it, squeezing love out. The long arctic night without sunshine, so that you must light a bonfire in the dark wood. The crackle of the flames had been like the crackle of breaking ice. The sweat started out on her forehead and she found that they had passed out of the happy wood into the church-yard and that she was looking at the very spot where she had seen the frail figure stooping over the grave.

"Was a child ever buried there?" she asked. "Look, there, under that crab-apple tree."

'Yes. Ten years ago," said Parson Hawthyn.

"And was the grave violated?"

"I feared so."

"You made no enquiries?"

"The soul of the child was safe and enquiries would have distressed the parents. If it was that poor woman, I prayed for her. You have been to see her today? There now, my dear, be careful of the water. Let me carry it while you open the gate."

She opened the churchyard gate and shut it, and then stood waiting for him while he carried the pitcher to the parsonage. She rubbed her hot cheeks ruefully, for she had betrayed herself in spilling the water. When he came back he smiled to see her rosy face. "My dear," he said, "your transparency delights my old heart. You are not yet, thank God, a subtle woman."

He limped along beside her talking of the blackberries at the bottom of his garden, for he was not an inquisitive man. His one leading question had been asked with a purpose. The misery of Mother Skipton was one of the clouds. If Froniga visited and pitied her he might know one day where to look for an ally. It was Froniga herself who brought the conversation back to its starting-point.

"What do you believe, sir, about black witchcraft?"

"I hold the accepted view," he said gravely. "I believe that evil spirits who have left this world, but desire to continue their evil practices within it, take possession of men and women who are willing to yield themselves for that purpose."

"It is also believed by many that only by burning the body of the black witch or warlock can you destroy the evil, and therefore the burning is justified. Do you believe that too?"

"Certainly not," said Parson Hawthyn. "Burning was never the Gospel method for the casting out of devils."

"But is burning so much worse than beheading or hanging?" asked Froniga. "Surely you don't disapprove of those?"

"My dear, I have already told you that I disapprove of nothing. I loathe, detest, hate and abominate the block, the gibbet, the rack, the pillory and the faggots with equal passion," said the old man vehemently. "Not only are they devilishly cruel but they are not even commonsense. They do not lessen the evil in the world, they increase it, by making those who handle these cruelties as wicked as those who suffer them. No, I'm wrong, more wicked, for there is always some expiation made in the endurance of suffering and none at all in the infliction of it."

Froniga was startled into complete silence. Never before had she heard such extraordinary statements. They had left the village and were taking the short cut through the fields to her cottage, walking more and more slowly as they became more argumentative. Looking at him she saw that Parson Hawthyn's usually gentle face had become stony with rage. Even his voice had become hard and rasping. She wondered how he proposed that law and order should be maintained in the land without those props of society that he had mentioned.

"I grant you we must have prisons," he growled. "Humanely administered. Even then I tremble for the souls of the gaolers. We are all of us so near the beast. Look at yourself, a lovely and cultured lady, yet able to sleep at night, calm as a white unicorn, with a loaded gibbet not four miles from you. Look at myself, walking with the same lovely lady and behaving like a mangy old bear with a sore head."

He looked himself again. His growling turned to chuckling and she laughed too, but she was not quite mollified, for she had always congratulated herself upon being an unusually humane woman.

"We all of us need to be toppled off the throne of self, my dear," he said. "Perched up there the tears of others are never upon our own cheek."

The anger went out of them both and they walked silently through the grey-gold twilight. The trees round Froniga's cottage had taken purple veils to themselves and from out of the shadows came the white form of Pen to welcome her mistress. The birds had gone to sleep and the only winged creatures were the moths, furry brown, or white with the greenish tinge of lilies upon their whiteness, or the faint gold of corn. The first drops of rain fell as gently as the touch of their wings.

"May I know for whom you will mix the potion?" asked Parson Hawthyn diffidently. "I would not intrude upon your secrets, Froniga, but I would be glad to add my poor prayers to yours."

"It is for Joe Diggar's convulsions," said Froniga, and the truth compelled her to add a little tartly, "The words I say over my potions are not what you would call prayers."

"Are they not?" said the old man. "Whatever you say, you offer it, do you not, together with yourself and your labour, for the well-being of the child?"

"Yes, I do that," said Froniga.

"I'll do the same tonight in the church. You can think of me there, and I will think of you. Now don't laugh and say there is no labour attached to my part of the bargain. The labour of keeping my body out of my bed, after nine of the clock, is greater at my age than you would believe at yours. But remember, Froniga, the well-being of the child may not necessarily include the prolongation of his earthly life. Dominus vobiscum, my daughter."

She put the elderberries to simmer in the spring-water over the fire, ate her supper and washed the dishes. Then she strained the liquid from the berries and bottled it in a clear crystal bottle, murmuring her spells as she did so, reaching out to the good spirits, and especially to that one good spirit whose power was hers as she murmured to them. They liked to do good on earth, but they could not, she believed, without the loan of her spirit and her body. What danger could there be for her? She thought of Parson Hawthyn with a spirit of irritation that passed quickly into a sense of vivid companionship. Her own work done she sat down, shut her eyes and tried to see him where he was in the church. Where did he kneel? At the altar? By the tomb of her little grandmother? Our Lady's niche? But she could see nothing, only darkness, and she abandoned the attempt. Darkness, she imagined, was what he would prefer her to see, and as she let it possess her she found surprising strength in it. There was darkness and darkness, one of life and one of death, and this of life was good.

THE FIRE OF FORGIVENESS

IT so happened that Tom and the ponies had betaken themselves to the far side of a haystack, to keep out of the wind, and Robert did not see them as he dismounted and tied Diamond to the churchyard gate. He walked slowly up the path to the church porch. His heart felt like a stone, it was so heavy, and the hammer-strokes of pain beat so ceaselessly on his temples that he felt bewildered and unsure of himself. "Lord, give me strength," he prayed again, and pushed the door open.

For a moment, with the sound of the children's voices in his ears and the colour and sunlight dazzling his eyes, he did not believe what he saw. This was some feverish dream. He shut his eyes for a moment, for the sunlight on the silver cross was blinding, but when he opened them it was still there, and so were the popish images decked out in gaudy berries and greenery. And Parson Hawthyn was sitting smiling on a bench, and beside him, smiling too, was Froniga. At sight of her glowing beauty a surge of hot passion went through him, and then came anger, such tearing anger as he had never known. Something seemed to break in his aching head and all power of control left him. All that was in him came surging out: his cruelty, his zeal and new-found strength, his suppressed and wounded love, and his anger. Like an avenging angel he went with powerful strides to the altar and took the cross from it, and tossed the flowers upon the ground. He carried the cross to the door and flung it outside. Then he took the stable and all the little figures in it, and the straw, and tossed them out into the churchyard too. He came back and shouted to the terrified children to bring out the greenery and garlands and the rest of the images that were defiling God's house, and reaching up he himself swept a row of little birds from a window-sill and hurled them through the door. He went to the screen and kicked the painted figures of the saints, soiling the soft colours of their robes. His eyes blazed, but his face was white as paper.

Parson Hawthyn and Froniga stood together, the old man trembling, Froniga frozen, and looked at him as though he were a stranger. Some of the children, huddled against them in fear, began to cry. Courage and control came back to Parson Hawthyn. "Don't cry," he said to the children. "There must be neither tears nor strife on Christmas Eve. We have had a happy hour. Do what the squire tells you. Take the fir branches and the little figures outside." Then, as a few of the older boys obeyed him, he turned round upon Robert and said sternly, "Robert, bring back the cross. The rest is of no importance, but the cross must come back to the altar."

But Robert did not look at him; indeed, he did not hear him. With his arms full of fir branches and holly he strode out into the churchyard and gathering everything together in a heap he took his tinder-box from his pocket and set fire to the dry hay and branches. Then he strode back to the church again. In the porch he was halted, as hands caught and held him.

"Are you mad, Robert?" asked Froniga. The shock had seemed to turn her to stone, but now that it had passed she was so angry that her fingers bit cruelly into Robert's arms. Yet her voice was cold and it pierced him. He had not heard Parson Hawthyn, but he heard her, though her voice seemed to him to come from a great distance. His arms, that had been struggling against her grip, were suddenly still, his eyes met hers and a childish bewilderment came into them. Pity was mixed with her anger. "You don't know what you are doing," she said more gently. "Think what you are doing and stop behaving like a madman."

She took her hands from his arms, and ran back into the church, for she could see Parson Hawthyn groping to pick up the scattered flowers before the altar, and he appeared to be groping sightlessly.

Her wide skirts and her cloak had hidden the two children behind her. Robert, now that her hands no longer held him, felt suddenly lost and unsteady. His eyes, that had been looking into hers, looked still where she had been, but it was a full minute before he saw Jenny and Will standing huddled in the corner of the porch, two small forlorn figures holding hands and looking at him. Will's mouth was open and his eyes were as round as an owl's. When they met those of his father they dropped. In a flash Robert saw Will's face when he had brought him his sword and they had smiled at each other, and then again he saw Will's face now, with the mouth so stupidly open and his eyes looking on the ground. And then it was Jenny's face that he saw, white and cold. Her lips were closed tightly and her eyes stared at him with no recognition in them. "Jenny," he whispered and held out his hand to her. She did not shrink away, but there was still no recognition. Though it was only for a couple of minutes, it seemed to Robert that he stood there for an eternity looking at his children. It did not seem to him possible that the Lord could have let them be there, could have let this happen. The Lord had forsaken him.

A boy was pulling at his sleeve and trying to tell him something. Other boys were running in and shouting, and the children who were still in the church were running out and falling over each other in the porch. Outside he could hear cries and the crackle of flames. Froniga had taken hold of his other arm and was pulling him out into the churchyard. He heard her crying out, "Jenny, keep the little children in the church." And then he was running with her down the path towards the churchyard gate, where Tom was already unfastening the terrified Diamond and taking her to a place of safety with the ponies.

It had not rained for some while and the bonfire he had kindled had soon taken hold of the dry hay and branches, and then the little wooden figures. The wind had caught up the flames into long streamers of fire and the flying sparks had blown on to the dry thatch of the parsonage, and it was blazing. Men from a nearby farm and women from the cottages came running, and in a few moments they had formed a chain of buckets from the nearest well and were working with a will. But it was hopeless. The little cottage was built mostly of wood and it burned like a torch. The flames leapt up against the dark driven clouds and streamed away with them before the wind. There were only fields south-east of the parsonage and the wonderful mercy of that morning was that no other home was destroyed, and no one was hurt except Robert, who went into the blazing cottage to try and pull out some of Parson Hawthyn's beloingings. He rescued no more than the old man's table and chair, and a plate with flowers upon it that he thought might be a special treasure, before he was seized and dragged away. "Do not risk your life, Robert," said Froniga sternly. "You cannot undo what you have done by burning yourself as well as the house. Look at your hands!"

He had burned them badly, but he felt no pain, and he had felt no fear when he went into the burning house. He had felt nothing but the longing to die there in the flames, that he might not again have to face his children or Parson Hawthyn. The Lord had forsaken him and he was in hell. Why could he not be allowed the flames of hell? Instead of that he found a kindly crowd about him. Someone had fetched salves and linen from the farm and Froniga was binding his hands. The little house was now a smoking ruin and Parson Hawthyn was thanking him courteously for saving his treasures. "That plate was my most valued possession," he said, smiling at Robert. "And the chair and table I valued greatly." None can lie more convincingly than the saints, when they feel that once in a way a lie is called for. The happy smile on the old man's face was no indication of the misery that was in his heart. Though he kept smiling, and saying to those about him the things he ought to say, his personal bereavement was just now very bitter. He did not mind in the least that the cottage had gone, and for the moment he had forgotten all that had happened in the church, but his books were burnt, including the book that had had "Charles R." written on the flyleaf. He did not know how he was to bear it. If only Robert had thought to pull out his books.

For the villagers and most of the children pleasurable excitement had now taken the place of alarm. They were used to fires, for with homes built so largely of wood and thatch they were a common occurrence, but what they were not used to was the squire taking leave of his senses. This was something quite new. The tenor of life's course had been delightfully interrupted. This was better than the war, for the war was at a distance, but the squire going mad was under their very eyes. It was obvious from the looks of him that he was mad, so they felt little indignation at what he had done. It was on a par with old Sam Tidmarsh flinging all the mugs of ale out of the inn when he was drunk. They all wanted to help Robert to his horse, and lift Jenny up in front of him that she might take the reins that he could not hold with his burned hands, so that Diamond could take him home. Froniga mounted Baw, for she was going with them. Margaret would never be able to care properly for Robert, or for the children in the state of bewilderment and shock that they were in. It was hard on Margaret, but she must go.

"You must come too, sir," she said to Parson Hawthyn. "You must come to the manor."

Robert was sitting his horse staring at the ruins of the parsonage, and now he looked down at the old man standing by his stirrup. "Let me make that much reparation," he said hoarsely.

Parson Hawthyn smiled at him. "It's not out of bitterness that I refuse," he said, "but because there is another house in my parish where I think it is my duty to go." He paused, drew nearer and said, "Robert, do not take this to heart. You did what you conceived to be your duty, and from the darkness that is our honest conception of light God in His mercy always brings some good."

Robert did not hear a word, but he was aware of the old man's forgiveness and was crushed by it. He bowed his head and sat inert upon his horse. Jenny took charge, turning Diamond round and heading courageously for home, with Froniga, Will and Tom riding after her. Parson Hawthyn watched them go pitifully, then turned to his parishioners.

"The services will be as usual tomorrow," he said briskly. "And the bells will be rung."

WHITE WITCH AND BLACK WITCH

SHE ran home and fed the cat. No matter who was dying, she never forgot Pen. She was not ashamed of loving animals so much, but sometimes she was a little ashamed of loving human beings so little in comparison. She did not feed herself; there was no time for that. Then she packed her basket with the remedies she might need. Her foresight knew now that the old man was very ill, but she did not know what was the matter with him. It might be the plague, and she put angelica in the basket, for it was invaluable for the plague as well as for flatulence, whether the patient chewed the root or drank the distilled water of the herb. It was called after the angel who had revealed its healing properties to a holy monk in a vision. Or perhaps Parson Hawthyn's heart had failed with so much tramping about the countryside, and she packed a bottle of the heart cordial compounded of borage, bugloss, calamint, harts-tongue, red mint, violets, marigolds, saffron and sugar boiled in white wine. In any case she knew he had fever and she packed a bottle of elder-flower water. To ease pain she had a bottle of borage flowers steeped in the oil of sweet almonds. The herbalist Thomas Hill had been a great believer in this latter remedy. "The flowers of borage," he had written, "steeped for a time in the oil of sweet almonds, and after the wringing forth of this, tenderly applied to the stomach, and region of the heart, do marvellously comfort the weak patient." Then she ran upstairs, took the blankets from her bed and fastened them into a bundle, with strips of material for poulticing inside it. She poured broth that she had made into a leather bottle and put that too in the basket. She had just put her cloak about her when she saw the snowdrops in their bowl upon the hearth and picked them up with a cry of joy. They had opened right out in the warmth, showing their golden hearts within the delicate veinings of pure green. She looked hungrily at the splash of green, shaped like a new moon, upon the outer side of the inner petals. When she saw the new moon she always knew that, whatever the weather, spring would not fail to come. She twisted some thread from her spinning-wheel round the little bunch and dropped it in the basket, lit her lantern and went quickly to the door.

Half-way to the cottage, walking as fast as she could over the frozen ruts of the lane, she saw another lantern coming towards her. She knew who it was and quickened her pace still more, and at the bend of the lane the two women met.

"I was coming to fetch you," said Mother Skipton. "Parson Hawthyn has been very ill for three days now."

"Then why did you not fetch me three days ago?" demanded Froniga, hurrying on in breathless anger.

Mother Skipton gave no answer, but looked at Froniga with hatred. Froniga felt a gust of joy within her, for Mother Skipton was jealous of her. She loved Parson Hawthyn enough to be jealous of the other woman's healing power. And now that her own had failed she loved him enough to fetch Froniga rather than let him die. The woman from whom Froniga had endeavoured to borrow a skull four months ago had been incapable even of jealous love.

"What is it, and what remedies have you tried?" asked Froniga.

"It is fever, but not the plague. I think he will die tonight. He would have none of my remedies, except a little camomile tea. But unknown to him, secretly, I have practised every healing art known to me. I have practised arts that I have never known to fail. Yet they have failed."

"If you mean that you have invoked the powers of evil, and in particular of that evil spirit who possesses you, to prolong the life of a man who inch by inch is forcing your evil out of you, of course you have failed," said Froniga impatiently. "What did you expect?"

They had reached the cottage and went in. It was bitterly cold. There was a wood fire burning, but it was smoky and sullen and the wind was blowing the smoke back into the room. Near the ill-fitting door the damp that had seeped up into the hollows of the earth floor had formed a film of ice. Near the fire it was an evil-smelling scum. Owing to the weather the jackdaw had been brought indoors and squawked raucously from his cage. The horrible little room stank more than ever of bitter poverty, but Froniga found that she could draw her breath more easily than she had before. The evil was less stifling. Mother Skipton lit a guttering candle, handed it to Froniga and opened a door in the wall, "Go up alone," she said curtly. "There is no more I can do. If you fail now yours is the shame."

"Heat me some water, please," said Froniga. Then she climbed up the steep stairs that came up directly into the garret, hardly bigger than a cupboard, where Parson Hawthyn had lived and slept all these last weeks. He had been lying in the dark until she came to him. She held up her candle and looked about her in horror. The rotting thatch had been stuffed with rags in places, but even so much water must have dripped through in wet weather. The floorboards were rotting too and smoke from the fire below came up through the holes. Fungus grew in the corners of the room. It was almost as cold as it was outside, and the crazy little cottage shook in the wind as though it would fall to pieces. Parson Hawthyn had lived in poverty and austerity in his parsonage, but he had had the modicum of comfort that preserves life. No old man of gentle birth and upbringing could have been expected to live through such a winter in conditions such as these, and he had been working beyond his strength in caring for his people and had been fighting a spiritual battle in this place. One glance at the old man told her he was near to death. He lay on a low wretched bed, covered with his cloak. The fever had abated, she thought, but his pulse was feeble and his skin cold and clammy to her touch. Though his eyes were open he did not answer when she spoke to him. He may have known she was there, she felt that he did know, but the power of communication with those about him had left him. Froniga wrapped him in the blankets she had brought, and then knelt beside him chafing his cold hands with hers that were nearly as cold. For she felt hopeless. This was the bitterness of death, these hours when a soul drifted in loneliness, beyond the power of help in this world and not yet received into the other. Froniga felt near to weeping for she had come too late.

Then she realized that her cold hands were beginning to glow and that within her there was that springing joy. Through her warm hands she and the old man seemed fused into one. Something that still lived intensely in Parson Hawthyn had communicated with the same thing in her. His delight in the service of his fellow men and her delight in life and all creatures, though the one was purged of self-will and the other was not, were akin. Fundamentally what they both adored was God, and now their love was burning so strongly within them that flame was lit from flame. Froniga began to understand something of a love like Parson Hawthyn's. Through the past weeks she had exulted to feel herself the instrument of love, had glowed in her own usefulness, but now she felt shame at the memory of her pride. Not in her manner would the old man have offered himself, his life or, if that failed, his death, for the woman downstairs, and if she was to save him now, it must be in his manner and not in her own. She must put aside her pride in her power, her wish to succeed where the other woman had failed, put aside even her selfish longing that he should live merely because she would miss him if he died. She must use this strong love that was being kindled in her in the way that love willed. His hands were growing warm now in her own but it was he, almost at the point of death, who was the channel and not herself. With a strange, strong, desperate effort she tried to free herself from herself and offered what she had dragged away. Then she took her hands from Parson Hawthyn's and got up. She had been kneeling by him for only a few minutes, yet it had seemed long. Her knees were shaking and she looked like an old woman. She went quietly out of the room and felt her way down the rickety stairs.

"I think he will rally," she said.

"An apothecary would say it was impossible," said Mother Skipton, "but no doubt your spells are more potent than my own."

There was venom in her tone, but she had heated the water. Froniga took the remedies she had brought from her basket and showed them to Mother Skipton. "I used no spells, but I brought these," she said gently. "Would you like to use them?"

"*I* use them?" asked Mother Skipton sharply.

"I have come here only to help you," said Froniga. "I will not go to Parson Hawthyn's room again unless you need me. Since he has offered himself, in life or death, to serve you, he would prefer that you, not I, should serve him."

"I know these remedies," said Mother Skipton. "And I know how to use them. I was a herbalist once, and in my youth I did much nursing of the sick. But what use is anything without warmth? I am nearly at the end of my wood, and it is damp."

"I have dry wood and sea coal at home," said Froniga. "I'll go to the inn for help and the men shall bring it down to you. A good fire here, and the door to the stairs left open, and the heat rising through the cracks in the floor will warm the room above."

She went out into the dark again and did what she had said she would do. The men carried the wood and sea coal and she carried all she had been able to lay her hands on in her cottage that would help either Mother Skipton or the sick man. All the night she stayed humbly in the kitchen, keeping the fire burning, heating broth for Mother Skipton when she came downstairs, looking after her in all the ways she could. And, astonishingly, Parson Hawthyn lived through the night and rallied. The next day she went home for a little while to look after her cottage and Pen, but she came back and sat with him for some hours while Mother Skipton slept. He was sleeping too and did not know that she was with him. As soon as he showed signs of waking she fetched Mother Skipton. That night she came downstairs and said to Froniga, "He is sleeping again and he will live."

"Are you sorry or glad?" asked Froniga.

"How can you ask such a question?" demanded Mother Skipton indignantly. "He saved my life."

"And if he gets well you will have to let him do it again," said Froniga. "Do you want that?"

"I don't know what you mean," said Mother Skipton curtly.

They were sitting together by the fire now, talking in low voices so as not to disturb the sick man. Above them on the mantelshelf the bunch of snowdrops, that Froniga had put in water in a cracked cup, shone as though it had light within itself.

"Yes, you do," said Froniga. "He will not be content with

having saved the life of your body unless he can save the life of your spirit too, and you have lived with him long enough to know how immensely precious yours is in his sight. If he is to go on living in the body merely to watch the death of your spirit, it would have been less cruel to let him die."

There was a long silence, and then Mother Skipton said in cold misery, "It is too late."

"Why did you come to church on Christmas Day?" asked Froniga.

"How do you know I did that?" demanded Mother Skipton.

"I saw you going away," said Froniga. "And I will tell you why you were there. You came because Parson Hawthyn had woken in you a longing for the days when you had not yet chosen evil for your good. If it had been too late you would not have been capable of longing."

"You do not know what you are talking about," said Mother Skipton. "If souls in hell were incapable of longing they would not be in hell. That *is* hell—longing for what you've thrown away and can never get back. I was a woman who wanted power. Through what stages I passed from white to black witchcraft I need not tell you, but they were all governed by the passion to possess power over the bodies and souls of men. At last, I liked to kill. But power is a devil who turns round on you at last. You possess it, then it turns and possesses you. Then power becomes powerlessness. I am far too tired now to change my way of life."

Her words had come in a sudden quick strange burst of speech, but now her voice died away into an exhausted silence. The dull hopelessness of her despair made Froniga feel cold and sick. The night pressed upon her and the squalor of the room where they sat. She was sinking herself into the other woman's powerlessness. Then, as though she were dragging herself up out of some morass of mud, she roused herself and said, "I believe I can guess what you heard when you knelt in the porch, listening by the crack of the door. 'Though thou hast been benighted till now, wintered and frozen, clouded and eclipsed, damp and benumbed, smothered and stupefied till now, now God comes to thee.' You heard that. Can't you believe it?"

"You talk nonsense," said Mother Skipton. "The old man talks nonsense. God does not come to lost souls."

"He has come," said Froniga. "In His servant, the old man, He has come. Can you not just do what the old man tells you to do? Not for your own sake, but for his in sheer gratitude. Is that so hard? I could help you. I know one thing he has told you to do and that you have not done. I'll do it for you. When you go upstairs give me the key of that cupboard there and I will open it, take away all that is in it and destroy it."

All Mother Skipton's lethargy and powerlessness left her. She was on her feet in an instant, her eyes blazing, her face twisted into snarling lines, her thin fingers curving like claws. It was as though something within her were suddenly awake and shaping her body to its will. Froniga had never felt so sickened and terrified. She had managed to get to her feet too, but she could not escape, though involuntarily she put up her hands to protect her throat as the other woman sprang at her. Then abruptly her fear vanished and her hands flew out from her throat and clasped the clawing hands of the other woman, holding them firmly. Mother Skipton struggled fiercely for a moment, and then went limp. It seemed to Froniga that only their hands locked together kept her on her feet. Froniga looked dazedly at their clasped hands. It was not she who had acted with such lightning quickness but the love within her to which she had yielded herself. She seemed to be leaning wearily against its strength, with the other woman drawn away from what had possessed her and into her own being, as though she and her sister were one.

Upstairs there was a weak and bewildered cry, like a child's. The old man had awakened and did not know where he was. Froniga gently withdrew her hands. Mother Skipton took the key that hung from her waist and dropped it on the floor. Then she turned without a word and went to him.

Froniga shut the door at the bottom of the stairs and unlocked the cupboard. The sickly stench that she remembered flowed out of it, nearly choking her, and her terror returned. Yet she did what she had to do. She took off her big apron and spread it on the floor and she began to take the things that were in the cupboard out of it and put them on her apron. Her limbs felt as heavy as lead and her fingers were cold and fumbling so that she moved with fearful slowness. The evil that oppressed her, that was here with her in this room, pressed upon her as a great wind does in a nightmare. She felt that she was giving ground, not gaining it, and she was in an agony that Mother Skipton might come downstairs again before she had finished. Yet she continued to take the things out of the cupboard: the skull of a child, another skull, the mandrake root, the phials that contained she knew not what, though some she thought held blood, and others poisons, wax images cruelly pierced with long thorns, and some mildewed old books. She had taken them all out at last and then, with some confused remembrance of the room in the Bible that had been cleansed of the evil spirit but left empty, she put the snowdrops in the open cupboard in their place. Then she tied the evil things up in her apron, put on her cloak and dragged the heavy bundle to her shoulders, holding it by the strong linen straps of her apron. She went to the door, opened it and went out.

A FALLEN SPARROW

HE went into the garden to cut the flowers for the church vases, but on his way to the daffodils was deflected by the sight of a dead hedge-sparrow lying on the lawn. Shame upon Orlando. Well fed though he was, he did occasionally forget himself and kill from wanton cruelty. A stab of pain went through John as he bent and picked up the small body, still warm . . . Not a sparrow falls to the ground . . . The little bird wore a sober livery and in the company of a bullfinch or a yaffiingale one would not have looked at him twice, yet lying there in his palm he seemed to John incomparably beautiful. The back and wing feathers were of different shades of brown, tender, warm colours, the throat and soft breast a silvery slate colour. The bill was slender and exquisitely curved and the little legs glowed bright orange. A short while ago his eyes had been as bright as the drops of water on the apple-tree, but now they were filmed. He would not again utter his thin pretty little song, and the children would not this year find his nest of moss and roots with the eggs of pure bright blue. John had what Daphne considered a ridiculous, inordinate love of the creatures. When he came to himself he was out of the lane, the small corpse still in his hand.

His idea, he believed, had been to carry it right out of the garden, so that Winkle should not find it and grieve; for Winkle felt like her father about the creatures . . .

He mounted the arc of the bridge, stooped and picked something up. He brought it back and showed it to Michael.

"A hedge-sparrow," said Michael. "The dun-coloured birds are the most beautiful, don't you think? I'd rather have that little chap than a goldfinch any day."

John picked a dock leaf, laid the bird gently on it and then launched the small boat upon the river. Borne by the current it floated slowly away towards the sea.

"The Lady of Shalott," said Michael, a little breathless with suppressed laughter.

"I think it was the cock," said John with extreme gravity. "Though there's so little difference in the plumage that it's difficult to tell . . . It would be such a pity if a child saw it," explained John. "Children grieve over these things."

ROOM AT THE INN

B UT Nadine's unbelief had not prevented her from agreeing wholeheartedly with George's proposal that they should turn their unused coachman's quarters into a comfortable little flat, suitable as a winter home, and invite Malony and Annie-Laurie to stay with them for always. Whoever they were, she liked and trusted them, and last night she and George had made the proposal, and after one hurried strange glance at each other they had asked if they might think it over. They had given no

136

answer as yet. Annie-Laurie had been very quiet all day, and Malony had made his jokes with difficulty. Nadine looked at her watch. It was three-thirty. In another hour or so their first real guests would be arriving; for the personal friends who had hitherto stayed with them had hardly counted. But these two—John Adair and his daughter—were strangers. And important strangers too. The familiarity of the name John Adair, when she received his brief business-like note asking for accommodation for an unlimited period, had sent Nadine to her *Who's Who*, to find to her dismay that he was what she had expected—John Adair the painter, a wealthy and famous man who would require to be fed as such; and she still had no cook. And the bath-water still showed a tendency to come out of the tap a curious shade of yellow-brown, and not always as hot as might be wished. A crease of anxiety showed between Nadine's eyebrows as she looked at her watch. She had an uneasy feeling that the offer she and George had made to Malony and Annie-Laurie had upset them in some way, and that they might perhaps take themselves off just at the moment when they were most urgently wanted.

There was a tap at the door.

"Come in," said Nadine.

Annie-Laurie entered softly and came and stood by Nadine's chair. She looked neat and fresh in her flowered overall, but her old-young face looked strained and weary.

"Yes, Annie-Laurie?" asked Nadine.

"If you please, Mrs. Eliot, my father and I think it would be best if we were moving on now."

"But Annie-Laurie, you surely won't leave me just when I have guests coming?"

"We'll stay another week."

"A week's not long. Mr. and Miss Adair are coming here indefinitely."

"My father says—just another week."

"Then you have decided not to accept the General's offer of staying with us permanently?"

"No."

The monosyllable dropped bleakly, and looking up at

Annie-Laurie's face, Nadine saw it desolate. She pulled forward the little arm-chair.

"Sit down, Annie-Laurie, and let's talk this over."

"It would be best for us not to stay," said Annie-Laurie wretchedly; but she sat down.

"Listen, Annie-Laurie," said Nadine. "I am very fond of you. I—love you, I think."

She had not known she was going to say that. She wasn't the sort of woman who said that sort of thing. She had not even known, until she spoke, that she did love Annie-Laurie. But it was true. Astonished, bewildered, she put out her hand as though for support against the sun-warmed panelling. And again she had that sensation of a warm and living personality—the personality that had prompted her to speak as she had. She glanced at Annie-Laurie. The girl's face was white and wore again that sealed-in look that had struck Nadine so painfully on the day of her arrival.

"Your father would like to stay. It is you who have decided against it," said Nadine.

"How did you know that?" whispered Annie-Laurie.

"I felt it, somehow. Why, Annie-Laurie? I know you are fond of me."

A curious pulsation passed over Annie-Laurie's sealed face, as when the first breath from the south passes over a frozen world. It passed, but she could not regain the old stillness. She struggled, but Nadine's warmth had pierced right through her defences and beneath them the life was painfully quickened. But she did not cry. She pushed her thin hands up into her lovely gold hair and held them there as though she carried in her head a burden too hard to bear, and her eyes seemed dumbly beseeching Nadine to deliver her from its weight.

"You'll have to try and tell me a little about yourself, Annie-Laurie," said Nadine gently. "That tale your father told us, the plumbing business and the bathing-machines and all that nonsense, I didn't believe it. Nor do I believe that he is Irish. Tell me the truth about him."

Annie-Laurie's hands slipped to her lap. They were trembling, and she clasped them tightly. But Nadine had helped her over the first hurdle, and she could speak now.

"He was a comedian. He was on the halls, and in pantomime. We did acts together. He sang Irish songs and I sang Scotch ones, and we both danced, and he told funny stories. It got sort of second nature with him to talk Irish. He was an engineer before he went on the halls. He's clever. There's nothing he can't do, nothing he doesn't seem to know. We made a lot of money at one time. We had—everything."

Music-hall artists. Nadine was surprised at herself that she had not guessed that before. Ben, with his usual intuition, had described Malony as a troubadour, and had been wiser than she. Their bizarre appearance, vitality, adaptability and imagination were explained now. But the change-over from engineer to comedian was odd.

"What made your father go on the halls?" she asked.

"He couldn't keep his engineering jobs."

"Why not?"

"They didn't satisfy him—and then he drinks sometimes," said Annie-Laurie. Her hands had stopped trembling and her face was quite expressionless.

"But not now," said Nadine.

"Not since we've been here," said Annie-Laurie. "Something new, something that interests him, and he's all right for a bit. But when he gets accustomed to anything —"

"And that's why you think you ought not to stay with me?" asked Nadine gently. "You think he'd disgrace the Herb of Grace?"

"Not only Jim—Father. I would. I've been in prison. Wherever we go, whatever we do, it comes out."

The desolation in her voice seemed to open a sort of pit at Nadine's feet. She was shamed. Women like herself, sheltered, indulged, secure, beloved; and yet they dared to find life hard, they dared to pity themselves because the path they trod was strewn with pink rose-petals when their own choice would have been crimson. She hated herself. Her hatred choked her, and she could not speak.

"So you see why we must go," said Annie-Laurie.

Nadine took a quick decision.

"There's no need to go, Annie-Laurie, if you would like to stay." Annie-Laurie stared at her incredulously. "Whatever it was that you did, that is in the past. It is what you are now that matters, and what you are now, I trust. I trust you, Annie-Laurie; both you and your father."

Annie-Laurie took a deep breath.

"He's not my father."

Again Nadine put out her hand as though for support, and again the old woodwork warm in the sun was like the clasp of a reassuring hand. Yet really, she told herself, she ought to have guessed that with Malony so obviously younger than he looked. And Annie-Laurie, perhaps, much older.

"How old are you, Annie-Laurie?" she asked.

"I don't look it, but I'm over thirty," whispered Annie-Laurie.

She was looking at her hands clasped in her lap, her head bent, and Nadine could not see her face. She, too, looked at Annie-Laurie's hands. The knuckles were showing white through the sunburnt skin. She stretched out her hand and put it over them.

"I had to tell you," said Annie-Laurie. "I had to—after you'd said you trusted me—even though —"

"It's all right," said Nadine. "You can still stay, if you want to. You do want to, don't you?"

"Yes," said Annie-Laurie.

"Why?" asked Nadine.

"Because of you . . . and the house." She looked up at last, her adoration warm in her eyes, but her relief a thing of such intensity that she could not speak of it. "He stuck to me through it all," she said.

"You can't marry him?" asked Nadine.

"It's not possible," said Annie-Laurie. "But we're not really doing anything wrong—I can't explain —"

"Listen, Annie-Laurie," said Nadine. "What you have told me is between us. I will not speak of it to anyone—not even to my husband. And I will not speak of it to you again, either; but if at any time you would like to tell me more about yourself, then I shall be glad to hear it." She paused, but there was no answer, and Annie-Laurie was once more looking at her hands. "For your own sake, not mine."

Annie-Laurie looked up speechlessly, and the light and warmth that had been in her face were gone. She was sealed in again.

"Very well," acquiesced Nadine. "That's settled then. And keep a firm hold on your Jim. We don't want him to start drinking."

Annie-Laurie stood up, her usual poised and steady self, and smoothed her overall.

"I don't think he will . . . not here."

"Is 'here' so different from other places?"

"Yes. You're different. The General and the children, and Jill. He likes you all . . . and the house."

"What is it about the house that attracts you so much?" asked Nadine.

"It's so safe," said Annie-Laurie. "Seeing it that day from the river—well, you know what it looks like from the river, towering up above the grey wall. I thought that morning—one could be safe there."

"You're safe here," said Nadine gently. Annie-Laurie folded her lips tightly, and Nadine saw that she was about at the end of her tether. "Run along now," she said lightly. "Those guests will be here soon, and you've the tea to get."

Annie-Laurie vanished, and Nadine turned at once to her house-keeping books, to stave off what she knew was coming. But it was no good. By the time she had added up the butcher the reaction had set in. What on earth had she done? Well, why ask that? She knew perfectly well what she had done. She, the respectable wife of a distinguished husband, the mother of five young children, two of them boys at the most impressionable age, had of her own deliberate choice taken into her household a man who at any moment might start drinking and a girl who had been in prison, and the relationship between the two of them, though Annie-Laurie had assured her they were doing "nothing wrong", was, to say the least of it, odd. She put the meat aside and tackled the fish, but the fish didn't make her feel any better. She felt cold all over, and was astonished, when she looked up, to see that the sun was still shining. She had been mad, she told herself—stark staring mad. Well, it was too late now. The thing was done, and she must abide by it. What on earth would Lucilla say if she knew? She could not imagine what Lucilla would say; she only knew that Lucilla must never know. No one must know. She was used to keeping secrets—there was David. But how she hated concealments! They made one feel imprisoned, walled in. Poor Annie-Laurie! What was walled in there? The girl was obviously mentally and nervously in a bad state, and also afraid, or she would not have spoken as she had about the sense of safety that the house gave her.

"Well, you've done it," said Nadine to the house. "You pulled them in here to yourself just as you pulled in George and the children. You've got to defend us all now . . . 'from all adversities which may happen to the body, and from all evil thoughts which may assault and hurt the soul'."

She realized that she was praying, and was astonished at herself, for it was not her habit to pray, and far away, like an answer to her prayer, came the distant chiming of bells. This faint chiming was now one of the special sounds of this place, a part of it, like the slap of the ripples against the river wall, the crying of the gulls and the beat of the swan's wings overhead. It came from the bunch of bright bells that hung on the top of the mast on Malony's boat. Sometimes the wind made them chime, and sometimes Malony's tramping about and rocking the boat. The sound was extraordinarily beautiful, and to Nadine at this moment reassuring.

UNDERSTANDING

COUSIN MARY'S DIARY

IT has happened and I am home again. There's a sense of awe when the impossible thing that you refused has happened, and it's over, and you don't know whether you went on refusing and it happened just the same, or whether somehow you accepted. But anyhow it's over. But I am not as happy as I thought I'd be because when something you have dreaded comes to an end there's a sense of anticlimax, like dust in the mouth. All the crashing ruin, the falling and tumbling, are over, but the dust is horrible. They say it won't happen to me again but I expect they only say it to comfort me. But I must think it won't. I must be like the people who plant gardens and build houses all over again where the earthquake has been. At the back of their minds they know there may be another 'quake but with the front of their minds they plant gardens. I wish I had a house and garden of my own, in the country and quiet. Though it's the suburbs here it's never really quiet and all the people coming in and out make me so confused and sleepless and tired. I'd like to live in the deep country with my dear Jenny Kennedy, just the two of us; not with Father and Mother and their anxious looks, wondering what next. Jenny doesn't wonder what next, she just loves me and takes what comes. I can't marry with this thing hanging over me, and I'll never be able to do much because when I get tired the desperation comes. They've never understood that. They've always thought I was lazy. I'm not, only when I'm tired it comes. It wouldn't have happened like it did if Mother hadn't made me go to Paris with her. It was the noise and the heat. All those people chattering, the traffic, and the dreadful sin of the city pressing in on me. Father could give me a little house in the country if he wanted to. I've begged for it but he won't listen. And Mother says it's impossible, Father couldn't afford it. But I've that bit of money my godmother left me and he wouldn't have to add a great deal to it. If I were like Virginia and got married he'd give me a dowry and trousseau, as he did her. When God is cruel to you everyone else is cruel too. When he turns his back he turns the whole world with him."

The diary broke off abruptly and began again a few days later. "I oughtn't to have said that about God. I don't know enough about him. I don't even know if he exists. Only if he doesn't exist why did I refuse? When you say, I won't, you refuse somebody and when you say, yes I will, you say it to somebody. I remember now that I did accept, that night when I woke up in the hospital room and there was the nightlight burning, and the night nurse moving in and out, and I realized that I was sane again. I was so thankful that I said, yes, I'll do it. You might say that wasn't a real acceptance because what I'd refused had already happened to me. But yet it was. You can go on refusing even after it's happened to you, like the child who screams and kicks the door after it's been shut up in the dark room. Or you can sit quietly down in the dark and watch for the return of light.

"Now it's out. I have said I was sane again and that means that I was not sane before. I have written it down. For I'm to be honest in this diary. That's why I'm writing it. I'm writing this to help myself by speaking out exactly what's in my mind. I can't talk to people because this illness isn't like other illnesses; all that's worst in it you have to hide so as not to spread fear. And anyhow they wouldn't understand. I remember Mother didn't when I was a child, and screamed after I was in bed at night, and when she came and I said I was lying on stones, and the black walls were moving in, she said I was a silly child and gave me a biscuit. I threw the biscuit on the floor for I had wanted her to put her arms round me and tell me she knew about the stones and the moving walls. Only of course she didn't know.

"When did I begin to realize that other people don't wake up every morning in unexplainable misery, don't, as soon as they are ill or exhausted, become sleepless and desperate? People mean different things by desperation. I mean the terror of impending disorder. For disorder of mind, or body, is evil's chance. At least, I think so. It seems to me to be integration that keeps evil out. I don't know when it was, I only know I struggled to keep my difference hidden just so as not to be different. There is a sense of safety in being like other people.

"I scarcely remember how it happened after we came back from Paris, for it's all a blur, but I do remember the insomnia and trying to get out of the window to escape from the evil. The time at the Home I only remember as a confused nightmare. But it's odd, I do remember one thing very clearly. I remember who among the nurses was kind to me and who was not. It would be awful to have to go back there and I'm going to ask Father once more if I may live in the country with Jenny. Mother will be furious because Jenny's her maid, and a good maid, but I know that if Jenny has to choose between me and Mother she'll choose me."

The next entry was some weeks later. "Father refused. It wouldn't be good for me to mope alone in the country. What I need is cheerfulness about me. Plenty of distraction. I tried to explain that what I need is just not to be tired, but I couldn't get the words out and suddenly I began to cry, and he kissed me lovingly and told me to go with Mother and buy myself a new hat.

"That was a month ago and it's been a miserable month until yesterday, when Mother thought it was her duty to ask the queer old man to tea. He's staying at the Vicarage taking the services while the Vicar is having a holiday. The Vicar apologized about him. The man who should have come got ill and there was no one to be found but this old man. The Vicar has cut his holiday down from three weeks to a fortnight, and only one Sunday, because of being so apologetic about the old man. He's very old and eccentric, and he doesn't shave very well though one can see that he's tried. At tea he was by turns very shy and very fierce and he mumbled sometimes and dropped cake on the carpet. There were other people there and Mother was annoyed, and after tea she asked me to take him out in the garden and show him the sweet peas. He was like a child about the sweet peas, he enjoyed them so much, their colour and lightness and scent. He said he'd never had a garden and when I asked him where he lived I found it was in lodgings down in East London, and for years he'd been Curate at a church in the slums. He wasn't at all sorry for himself but I was sorry for him because he loved flowers and had no garden, and suddenly I burst out and told him how I longed to go and live in the country. He looked at our beautiful garden as though he wondered how anyone could want anything better, and then he looked at me very keenly out of his bright blue eyes and said 'Why?' The question came out so sharply and suddenly that I answered with the truth. I told him everything. It was the queerest thing that had ever happened to me because I take such infinite trouble to cover it all up. I hide it like a crime. And yet here I was laying it all out in front of him. I was like a criminal emptying his pockets. I took out everything. He was silent for a long time, rubbing his chin, and then he said, 'You're afraid of it?'

"It seemed such a silly question and I spoke sharply I think when I said 'Of course I am, I'm terrified.'

"'Why?' he asked. 'If you lose your reason you lose it into the hands of God.'

"I said, 'Why does God let us suffer like this?' and he answered, 'My dear young lady, how should I know? Job didn't know, but he repented in dust and ashes.'

"He wasn't helping me at all and I said crossly, 'I haven't done anything frightfully wrong. Nothing that calls for dust and ashes.'

"He said quietly, 'No?'

"I said, 'It makes one hate God.'

"He said, 'Where you've put him?'

"'Where have I put him?'

"'On the gallows.'

"And then suddenly he caught sight of a tortoiseshell butterfly drifting down the path and he gave an exclamation of incredulous joy and ran after it. When I caught up with him he was standing in front of the buddleia tree, which was covered with butterflies like it nearly always is, and he was speechless with wonder, his face as absorbed as a child's when the candles have been lit on the Christmas tree. It was almost as though the butterflies shone on him and lit his face. Or else it was the other way round. For a moment there seemed light everywhere, though it was a grey day. It was queer and I didn't want to move; until there was a sound of voices and we saw Mother and her guests coming out into the garden. The old man looked round at me and the light had been wiped off his face; it was puckered and distressed, like a sad monkey's, and he said to me in a hoarse whisper, 'My dear, I think I should be going,' and I realized that he was terrified of Mother and her guests. He must have been terrified all through the tea party, when he mumbled and dropped crumbs on the carpet.

"'Come this way,' I said. 'Round by the greenhouse. I'll say good-bye to Mother for you.' We went into the house by the side door and when we were in the hall he said to me, 'I think I had an umbrella. I feared thunder.' He had brought a baggy old umbrella tied with string and while he was fumbling to get it out of the stand he said to me, 'It's safe there, you know.'

"I said, 'The umbrella?' and he answered, 'No, no, no! Your reason. It's the only place where anything is safe. And when you're dead it's only what's there you'll have. Nothing else.'

"He had a round clerical hat, dusty and green with age. He put it on, gripped his umbrella in his left hand and held out his right to me. I held it and it was dry and rough and hot. 'My dear,' he said, 'I will pray for you every day of my life until I die.'

"Then he abruptly let go of my hand, turned his back on me and stumbled down the steps that led from the front door to the drive. At the bottom he turned round again and looking into his face I noticed that when he was neither eager nor alarmed his eyes had the most extraordinary quietness in them. 'My dear,' he said, 'Love, your God, is a trinity. There are three necessary prayers and they have three words each. They are these, "Lord have mercy. Thee I adore. Into Thy hands." Not difficult to remember. If in times of distress you hold to these you will do well.' Then he lifted his hat and turned round again. I stood at the door and watched him go. He had a queer wavering sort of walk. He did not look back.

"I went to the garden for I knew Mother would be vexed with me if I didn't go back to her guests, though I didn't want to. I walked soundlessly over the lawn towards two women who were standing in admiration before one of Mother's rose bushes, which was in full bloom. But they weren't looking at it. 'Horrible old man!' one of them was saying. 'Anyone can see he drinks. What was the Vicar thinking of to have him here? Better to have left us with no one. In and out of asylums for most of his life, I'm told.'

"I stood quite still. He hadn't told me. He'd stood aside, speaking only of God and me. I wanted to run after him but when I moved they saw me, and the one who had spoken blushed crimson and I had to go forward and speak to them and pretend I hadn't heard.

"And now it's night and I am in my room and writing down everything he said before I forget it. He said so little and he explained nothing. He couldn't. But it has come into my mind that what he couldn't explain is that treasure hid in a field in the old story. If one were to spend a lifetime digging for the treasure, and in this time of one's life not find it, one wouldn't have wasted the time. There would be less far to dig in the next time. Only one must possess the field, whatever it costs to buy it, and it has again come into my mind that fields are quiet places. And so I've got to have that home in the country with Jenny. My old man had the quietness within himself and I'll never know how he came by it. Perhaps for him outward quietness isn't necessary, but for me it is. I've never got on with Father and Mother. I've always been the one of their children they cared for least, and now I've brought this trouble upon them. Once the tussle is over it will be as much a relief to them as to me if we can live apart. I'll start fighting again tomorrow."

The beautiful handwriting broke off and did not begin again for another three months. The date was "October 14th" and under the heading Cousin Mary had written, "The Laurels, Appleshaw. My first night here and I can't sleep I'm so happy. I'll sit up in bed and write a little. Fighting Father and Mother nearly cost me another breakdown, but I managed to keep saying the three words of the three prayers and though they didn't mean a thing to me I kept my head above water and I brought the doctor round to my side. He told Father to let me do what I liked.

"It was Jenny who found this house. She has a cousin, a Mr. Postlethwaite, who lives here, and he told her about it. She came down to see it, by herself without telling anybody, and she liked it.

So when I was well enough she and Mother and I came down to see it and Mother thought it was awful but I knew it was home.

"And so here we are, and Mr. Postlethwaite is going to keep the garden in order and carry the coals for Jenny, and find someone to scrub the floors. But all the rest Jenny will do. She's always been a lady's maid and now she'll be doing everything. She's given up so much for me and there are times when I feel miserably guilty, and then at other times I realize that looking after me is as necessary for her as learning to be quiet and to dig are necessary for me. We just have to do it.

"I shall live and die here. Perhaps I shall never be well but this place will give me periods of respite that I would not have found in any other, and though I am able to do nothing else in this life, except only seek, my life seeming to others a *vie manquée*, yet it will not be so, because what I seek is the goodness of God that waters the dry places. And water overflows from one dry patch to another, and so you cannot be selfish in digging for it. I did not know anything of this when I began this diary and I don't know how I know it now. Perhaps it has something to do with the old man.

"It is quiet in this room. I've only been here a few hours and yet already I know my home so well. There are no curtains at my window for Jenny and I have only got the barest essentials as yet. I want to get the rest very gradually, old pieces of furniture to match this old house, just the right curtains and carpets. An old house that's come alive through the centuries is not just a shelter from the weather, it's a living thing and can be served. I could feel the life of this house as soon as I came through the door in the garden wall. And so there are no curtains at the windows and the moonlight is shining so brightly that I hardly need my candles, and when I lean forward I can see a sky crowded with stars behind that great tower. I'm glad I've come here in still, mellow October weather. The great lime avenue was thick with piled gold when we drove through it, but when the trees bent to possess us and I looked up at them I could see the blue sky through the gold leaves because though there were so many of them they were worn thin, like very old coins. The fields were blue and hazy and when we got to the village green I could smell bonfire smoke and blackberry jam boiling. The wistaria leaves are a fall of golden rain on each side of the pillared way and on the south side of the house the virginia creeper is scarlet on the wall. Down in the coppice at the bottom of the garden there are crab-apples and the haws are scarlet.

"I am learning it all by heart. I expect the winter will be hard in spite of the country snow like white fox fur wrapped about the house, filling the rooms with light. The snow will melt and it will be cold and wet and I shall be ill, like I always am, with the vile asthma and bronchitis, and I shall fall into black depression and perhaps desperation too, but it will pass and the spring will come with celandines and white violets in the lanes, and then the late spring with bluebells and campion and the wistaria coming out. And I shall learn the spring by heart, and then the summer, and I'll learn the bells and birdsong by heart, and the way the moonlight moves on the wall and the sun lies on the floor. I'll grow older and lose my beauty but the spring will not grow old nor the moon nor the snow. Who will live after me in this house? Who will sit in the little parlour reading by the fire? And then she will put out her lamp and come up to this room and light the candles and kneel by the bed to pray. I don't know who she is but I loved her the moment I walked into this room, for that was the moment that was timeless. I shall have my sorrows in this house, but I will pray for her that she may reap a harvest of joy. I will pray for her every day of my life, as the old man is praying for me."

Mary closed the book for that was all she would read tonight. It was as much as she could bear. She put out the lamp and went upstairs to bed. In her room she lit the candles in the two brass candlesticks, and knelt down beside the old-fashioned bed. It was only for the moment that it seemed strange to be kneeling, for those who had lived in this house during the past centuries had belonged to the years of faith and her body relaxed easily into their habitual posture. What should she say to her discarded God? Her childhood's prayers came to her mind but they were too infantile. But the old man's prayers were not infantile and she repeated them.

COMPANIONSHIP IN FEAR

"You ran away, Ben," said David.

"Yes," said the little boy, and hung his head.

David swung himself out along the tree trunk to sit by Ben. It was a rather perilous position in which to examine a precious volume, but a perfect one in which to face a terrible fact of life. The book might fall into the water at any moment, but all around them was such loveliness and peace, and in front of them, through a break in the trees, they could see a perfect view of the marshes, the sea and the sky.

"The pictures are perfectly horrible, old man," said David. "I don't blame you for panicking. I was scared stiff myself, and even Obadiah doesn't think them pretty."

Ben let out a shuddering sigh of relief. It was extraordinarily comforting that other people should be frightened too. Ben had all the horror of being abnormal of a supersensitive person. So often he had found that other people didn't feel about things as he did, and it made him feel very lonely. It was consoling to have David's companionship in fear.

"But you see, Ben," David went on, "they're not quite true. They're exaggerated. I grant you that death can be dreadful, but it's not as bad as this. You see, it was a sick man who drew these last pictures, and a healthy man who drew the first ones, and the truth about things is somewhere between the two. When we feel well and jolly we see the happy side of life, and are inclined to think that's all there is to it, and when we're sick we see the seamy side and are inclined to think that's all there is to it too. You've got to get both sides, and not exaggerate either of them, before you get the truth ... And even then you only get the shadow of it.'

Ben did not quite understand, but he took the book from David and began bravely to look at the pictures again, first the happy ones and then the awful ones.

But he found, this time, that the awful ones were not quite so awful as he had thought they were. He had not noticed, for instance, until David pointed it out, that in that picture where the dead soldiers lay line upon line like the furrows of a ploughed field the clouds above were formed of spread wings. And there were other comforting things, in the other pictures, that he had not noticed either until David showed them to him.

"How odd that I shouldn't have noticed," he said.

"The nice things aren't drawn in a noticeable way," said David. "Besides, you weren't looking properly before. The horror of the pictures stunned you and you didn't look them steadily in the eye, so to speak."

"Well, I have now," said Ben, "and it's not as bad as I thought." He gave a great sigh of relief. "I shan't think about it in the night any more; or if I do I'll remember the wings . . . Surely it's tea time?"

THE INNER REALITY

HILARY puffed at his pipe, and his eyes twinkled, but for a moment or two he said nothing. Then he said, "The other day we talked about throwing dust in the other fellow's eyes, and most of the time that is what we all do. Shall we do that now, or shall we try to get behind it?"

"For I should think the first time in my life I should like to try to get behind it," said Sebastian. "That, for me, is a volte-face, but I know that I have not long to live, and there are things I should like to speak about."

"You look better," repeated Hilary.

"I am. But all the same one knows."

"Some do," said Hilary. "I hope I do when my time comes. I should dislike taking a header, so to speak, into eternity. I would rather be like Dante's good mariner, who 'when he draws near to the harbour lets down his sails, and enters it gently with slight headway on; so we ought to let down the sails of our worldly pursuits, and turn to God with all our understanding and heart, so that we may come to that harbour with all composure and with all peace.'"

It was easy to see what had brought the quotation to Hilary's mind. From where they sat on their seat in the sun they looked across the flowers in the garden to the broad shining reaches of the tidal river. Quite close to them a boat rocked at anchor with sails down. It had reached a perfect haven.

"One cannot turn to God unless one finds Him," said Sebastian.

"At your worst hour you found something," said Hilary. "You must have found something, or you could not have come through."

"Nothing," said Sebastian. "Except at brief moments just a consciousness of world-suffering."

"Held within it. Supported by it and cleansed by it. And yet at the same time you were taking your infinitesimal share in the bearing up and the redemption," said Hilary. He asked no questions, but stated facts.

"I did not analyse it," said Sebastian.

"You do not analyse Christ," said Hilary quietly. "You find Him. Or perhaps it would be truer to say that He finds you; sometimes without your conscious knowledge. For the Christian, searching hour by hour through the days and nights, the months and years, if the time ever comes when he can say, 'By the grace of God I know what I know', what he experiences can seem more or less like a conscious finding; but for those who have not chosen to search, but whom yet He has chosen to find, when for a brief moment He speaks to them they call Him by another name: 'Christ, or whatever name is given to the secret kingdom of heaven in which we are and have this shadow of life, that shadow of the grave.' I seem full of quotations today. The fact is you other fellows, you poets and musicians, say these things so much better than the rest of us."

"The kingdom of heaven is a queer name to give to the 'huge debt of pain' that 'mounts over all the earth'," said Sebastian drily. "I am quoting now, you notice."

"I noticed," said Hilary. "I also noticed that you used the word debt. It is the right word. Pain and death are owed for sin. Christ paid the debt, and He is the debt, for it was His own life that He put down in payment. We offer His pain and death, and our own within His—of no value apart from His—for the redemption of the world. Forgive me for putting extremely badly what you have probably known all your life."

"Heard all my life," corrected Sebastian. "Heard, but not known. You have to relate information to experience before you can be said to know."

"Do you think now that you and I both know the same incommunicable thing?" asked Hilary.

"I think the occasional shaft of light in my darkness may have pierced its way through from your sun," said Sebastian. "I would not say that anything I have known approaches anywhere near what I believe is called the mystical experience; for that, as I understand it, is a direct apprehension of God by the mind, leading to a process of purging through which the loathsome demon of self in man is done to death. If that had been so I should have recognized your Christ and He would have made something of me by this time."

"No man can form any judgment as to his own state," said Hillary, smiling.

"I still hate."

"The last of the chaff," said Hilary. "You use strong words about the substratum of our being which is usually referred to with tender consideration as the lower self."

"I have seen it, corrupted by great evil, at close quarters," said Sebastian grimly.

"You saw it in others?" asked Hilary.

"In others," said Sebastian. "But now, God help me, I am beginning to see it in my own hatred."

"If you hated your persecutors, then there was not much to choose between you. If you hate a man more fortunate than yourself, then you deserve your misfortune. Is that how you feel now?" asked Hilary.

"Not quite as far as that yet," said Sebastian, smiling.

"Getting," murmured Hilary. "The grain lies sheer and clear. And if it is David whom you imagine you hate, I doubt if the contrasts between you are quite so deep as you imagine. Much like yourself. Much the same temperament. Always in trouble of one sort or the other."

Sebastian smiled. "And now, perhaps, in what seems to him the worst yet."

Hilary took his pipe from his mouth and was still and attentive.

"Merely my fancy, perhaps," said Sebastian.

"What made you fancy it?" asked Hilary gently.

"Merely a feeling I had that the man I hated was a dying man," said Sebastian. "Not in the physical sense, you understand. And then I read a poem I found in my room. You may know it, for you spoke of the chaff and the grain. Merely conjecture, as you see."

"You are probably right," said Hilary soberly.

Sebastian fancied that he felt deep hurt in him. "Forgive it that a stranger —" he murmured.

"No, it is not that," said Hilary quickly. "I am glad that your intuition has convicted me of blindness and dullness. Very good for me. I am troubled because I happen to be fairly comfortable myself at present, and I'll feel the worst sort of hypocrite if I try to tell him about the right and wrong way to endure. That had better be your job."

"Impossible to my ignorance," said Sebastian, smiling. "For myself, I have merely endured because there was nothing else to do."

"That is what he did before," said Hilary. "And broke."

"Had he a bad war?" asked Sebastian.

"A great deal better than most," said Hilary. "But the bombing of other men's homes and children was not the best war service for a man of his type."

Sebastian felt a little dizzy. Hamburg and the walls of flame. Hatred of David and a surge of sympathy for him, deeper than anything he had felt yet, had hold of him together.

"Thought about it too much," said Hilary.

"Yes," said Sebastian. "We do, men of our type. We think about the harm we do until we become monsters in our own eyes. That is good, you'll say; but we think about the monster until he has us circling about him as though he were some hideous little heathen god. If he stops there it can become almost a form

157

of devil-worship, and it is not worship the devil in us needs. But I am wandering from the subject of endurance."

"Not at all," said Hilary. "The right kind of self-knowledge calls for a good deal."

"In your war, the first, how did you endure?" asked Sebastian.

"My war was nothing," said Hilary hastily, "nothing at all compared with yours, or even David's. Yet I had a way, then, that helped with other things later. For there is always the Thing, you know, the hidden Thing, some fear of pain or shame, temptation or bit of self-knowledge that you can never explain to another . . . And even in those very few healthy insensitives who do not seem to suffer, a love of something—of their work, perhaps—that they would not want to talk about and could not if they would. For it is the essence of it that it is, humanly speaking, a lonely thing . . . Returning to the sensitives, if you just endure it is simply because you must, like a boil on the neck, or fret yourself to pieces trying to get rid of it, or cadge sympathy for it, then it can break you. But if you accept it as a secret burden borne secretly for the love of Christ, it can become your hidden treasure. For it is your point of contact with Him, your point of contact with that fountain of refreshment down at the roots of things. 'Oh, Lord, thou fountain of living waters.' That fountain of life is what Christians mean by grace. That is all. Nothing new, for it brings us back to where we were before. In those deep green pastures where cool waters are there is no separation. Our point of contact with the suffering Christ is our point of contact with every other suffering man and woman, and is the source of our life."

"You could put it another way," said Sebastian. "We are all the branches of the vine, and the wine runs red for the cleansing of the world."

"The symbols are endless," agreed Hilary. "Too many, perhaps. They complicate the simplicity of that one act of secret acceptance and dedication."

They were silent, and then Hilary said, "We have talked too much of the demon in men. There is the child too. It is an antidote against hatred to think of the child. The mask that a man shows to the world hides a frightened child, and the child hides the demon.

But it is the child who wins. The mask drops at death, and the demon is finally destroyed either in this life or another, but the eternal child in us lives on."

"Invariably?" asked Sebastian grimly.

"You are right. I am speaking too confidently," said Hilary slowly. "I believe it to be a matter for our choice."

"The demon might live on and the child die?"

The bright landscape seemed a little shadowed to them both, and Hilary did not answer for a moment.

"That is why the child is afraid," he said at last. "While the outcome is still in question the child is always afraid. I believe that that appalling possibility is the source of all fear."

"All frightened children need the comforting of love," said Sebastian.

FAITH

ILARY got George on the phone, told him to expect Malony when he saw him, and then lay back in his chair and stretched his feet luxuriously to the blaze. The room was becoming gloriously warm, and already the scent of coffee was creeping in, and the delicious smell of something frying. Hilary sniffed with appreciation, and just for the moment yielded to the pleasurable idea that he was one of those old coves who before the war used to live in luxurious chambers in Town, waited on hand and foot by a faithful manservant. Then he thrust the notion from him in horror and remembered that he hadn't said Evensong. He pulled his office book from his pocket, recollected himself and made a start, but the increasingly appetising smells from the kitchen kept insinuating themselves between him and his God, and he put the book back in his pocket and gave it up as a bad job. He was deeply humiliated. He had thought in his younger days that increasing age would mean increasing freedom from the weaknesses of the flesh, and yet here he was with his soul apparently at the beck and call of a frying-pan. However, the humiliation was salutary. That was the best thing about old age; it didn't leave you with much upon which to congratulate yourself.

Malony came back with a loaded tray. He had brought a second plate, but set it rather tentatively upon the table.

"You said, sir —?"

Hilary got up and pulled another chair forward.

"Of course I did. And drop the sir, will you, just as you've dropped your Irish accent? Chuck all the disguises for a little while. It'll rest you. You do me a great honour. It's not every day that I entertain a famous comedian to supper, still less have him waiting on me hand and foot. Gosh! What a superb fry! What on earth did you put in it?"

He bent boyishly over the dish before him. Malony had fried spoonfuls of powdered egg to crisp little fritters, had added the sausages disinterred from their coffins of sodden pastry, onion, parsley and potato, and had made of the dish a work of art. He had made crisp toast, too, and superb coffee. Hilary's thick glasses were misted by the steam from the hot dish, and he took them off to wipe them, smiling across at Malony as he did so. The man opposite, divided between anger and relief at the stripping away of his defences, his nerves jangling, was taken utterly aback by the extraordinary beauty of Hilary's eyes without their glasses, by their keen, straight glance, by the enveloping warmth of his utterly happy yet rather deprecating smile. The immense power of his goodwill, together with his personal humility, made a sudden unexpected appeal that got right under Malony's guard before he knew where he was. He wasn't out to do you good, this chap—he didn't think enough of himself for that—he was simply out to jog along beside you for a little, and pass the time of day, knowing you were down on your luck, and thinking a bit of companionship might not come amiss. And he was straight. He didn't say what he didn't mean. When he'd said that about an honour, he'd meant it. He'd got sense, too. Anything you told him would be in wise keeping.

"I don't say it's not a bit of relief to be Jim Harris for a bit," he said suddenly, helping himself to fry. "Though, mind you, I've worn so many disguises in my time that I slip 'em on and off like suits of clothes. And as for the sir, that comes naturally—I'm not like Annie-Laurie, who comes of good yeoman stock. I was born in a back street in Clerkenwell. My father kept a pub there. That's where I got the taste for drink that's been a curse to me all my life."

Hilary readjusted his glasses and attacked his supper.

"Goes with you like a dead hen tied round a terrier's neck," he said sympathetically. "Trips you up when you're down in the mouth about something, or so dog-tired you don't know how to drag along another step. Don't I know. With me it's a sort of luxuriating in the detestableness of myself—inverted pride. I take to it, as you to drink, when my faith fails me."

"Failure of faith," said Malony. "That's a queer thing, surely, for a man like you to suffer from. I thought faith was what a parson lived by."

"So it is," said Hilary. "It's what every man lives by. But you know how in the black moments it's always apparent failure of what you live by that gets you down. Only apparent, of course, for the mere fact that you're wretched because you think your faith's gone really means that you've got hold of it pretty firmly. If you had no faith you wouldn't care one way or the other, would you?"

"I wouldn't know," said Malony, with gloomy self-satisfaction. "I've no faith myself."

"You've all the marks of it. About the most selfless chap I ever met. Without faith in the possibility of something divine existing in humanity it beats me how you can slave for it as you do. What made you first take to the drink in Clerkenwell?"

"General ugliness of things. I was a romantic youngster. Thought life ought to be a lot different from what it was. Then a pal of mine let me down."

"There you are, then," said Hilary comfortably. "You believed in beauty, in loyalty. Drunk, you still believed in them. If you hadn't you wouldn't have been drunk. Have some more coffee. And push the fry this way."

Malony suddenly laughed delightedly. He had been so desperately cold, but now, with the coffee and the fire, he was warm. And he had been so utterly wretched—beyond the reach, he thought, of any laughter—but the droll appearance of Hilary, scanty grey hair rumpled, glasses misted by steam, elbows squarely out as he frankly and joyously attacked his meal, tickled his comedian's sense. Not that he was laughing *at* the fellow; that he would never do, after that glimpse of the man's essential quality that had been his when he took off his glasses; but he unexpectedly found himself laughing with him at the absurd pomposities of human nature. Of course faith and life were synonymous, and Hilary had been right to explode his conceited assertion that he could possess one without the other, even as he was delightfully right in making no secret whatever of the fact that a man of God can enjoy his food. Reserve, though life had forced it on him of late years, was not natural to Malony. It ebbed from him as he helped himself to more coffee, stretched his boots to the fire and leaned

165

back in his chair with a movement of exquisite relief; almost the relief of a man released from pain. Hilary, reaching for the coffee-pot and praying for guidance, recognized the signs. He was about to be told the story of Malony's life, and from the recitation of bare facts he must build up the framework, and out of his own experience and insight clothe it with flesh and blood of the living man; or else fail to help the man. He did not eat any more, and he poured his coffee black.

THE FAITH OF OLD AGE

THERE was a faint rustling behind him, nearer than that of the rushes, the murmur of a silk dress, and he got up and turned round with no sense of annoyance or apprehension but of inevitability, for whoever came had a right to come and belonged here. A very old woman stood looking up at the swans and listening to the lark. She had not seen him, and he thought that perhaps neither her sight nor her hearing was very good now, for there was a look of strain upon her face, as though the glory of the sky that was so clear for him was for her only a rumour. That, he thought, must be the hard part of old age, that slow relinquishment while still in this world of the power to see and hear the symbols. "For the eternal things of Him from the creation of the world are clearly seen in the things which are made." But when they are no longer clearly seen, and yet the soul has not passed on beyond them, was it as though she fell into a sort of nothingness? Or was the dying rumour of the lark ascending replaced by a new sort of certainty of things to come? He would like to ask this old woman. He was sorry for that look of strain upon her face, and instead of trying to escape he stood quietly where he was, waiting for her and enjoying the picture that she made.

She was tall, and the folds of her black dress fell gracefully. A white rose was tucked in her belt and a white lacy shawl had been flung over her head and draped her shoulders. She leaned upon an ebony stick and he saw the flash of diamonds on her left hand. She

looked like some great lady of the eighteenth century and seemed as perfectly in place against the background of Damerosehay as Eliot had looked yesterday, when Sebastian's fancy had seen him as an oil-painting glowing against the shadows of the house. But she was not a Rubens. The clear black and white, the stately dignity, made him think of Holbein's Duchess of Milan. But the Duchess was a young woman, and this woman was even older than he had imagined when he had first seen her.

She turned and saw him, and smiled as though he were an old friend whom she was pleased but not surprised to see here. "I'll have your arm to help me sit on that seat, Mr. Weber," she said. "I have difficulty in getting down when I am up or up when I am down."

He helped her, and they sat down as companionably as Meg and he had sat together on the other seat in the drive. She turned and looked at him, neither considering him as a problem nor pitying him, but simply accepting him and making him welcome. Her blue eyes had the same steady appraising glance as Meg's had, and Eliot's, but in spite of being a little clouded by great age, they saw much more. That sense of belonging nowhere, that had troubled him for so long, suddenly vanished. He settled himself more comfortably on the seat.

"That is how I felt when I first came to this house, before it was mine," she said.

"How did you feel, Lady Eliot?"

"Anchored."

"I have no right to feel that."

"Why not?" she said. "You have come where you are needed."

"Who needs me here?" he asked her, gently but yet with bitterness.

"Now, that is a very silly question," she said, answering his bitterness with a touch of asperity. "You should know better than most men that no great artist writes a note or word, or makes one stroke of a brush, that is not necessary to the perfection of the whole. Is God less intelligent than his creatures?" She stopped and smiled at him a little anxiously, her asperity vanishing in childlike uncertainty. "I do not see very well," she said.

"You have great insight," he said. "You knew of my sense of exile."

"Oh, yes, that," she said. "When you get old, and must lose your hold upon so much, there are new insights. I meant I was not sure that you were you, after all. But I see now that you are. I heard you play in Paris, between the wars. It was my last holiday abroad before I got too old to want to leave Damerosehay. David was with me."

"You cannot recognize me, Lady Eliot," he said. "It is not possible that I can bear the slightest resemblance, now, to the young man I was then. You recollect my name, perhaps. I did not bother to change it because I did not imagine that anyone would remember it."

"I did not remember the name until I saw you," said Lucilla. "You have changed less than you think you have. You know, however altered we may be by age or illness, there always looks out from us, now and again, the young creature we once were and will be again. And then I never remember any other pianist with hands just like yours, nor with that trick of resting them as you do, one within the other with palms upwards. I looked down upon them, I remember. You played the Waldstein. What an evening of delight you gave us! David and I said that we would never forget, and I have not forgotten."

Sebastian smiled. "He has."

"He was very young then. He will remember again. Something will remind him."

"I sincerely hope not," said Sebastian with vigour. "The young man that I was is dead and buried. Don't resuscitate him, Lady Eliot. Let him rot." Then he saw that the harshness of his tone had hurt her, and he made a gesture of apology. "Forgive me. I am afraid that my manners are a thing of the past."

"Then you should play again," said Lucilla severely. "Music recaptures the past."

"That is why I shall never play again," said Sebastian. "Even if my hands were not stiffened, as they are, I should never play again for that reason."

"How very ridiculous of you!" said Lucilla. "Do you imagine

that past happiness is lost? You will come round to it again when the circle is complete, and at the end of it all nothing will be eternally lost except evil."

"So they say," remarked Sebastian grimly. "Meanwhile, for most of us at present, it appears to be the good that is eternally lost."

"How can good be lost if it is remembered?" asked Lucilla. "It can be pain to remember, I know, but it is one of those pains that are incumbent on us, and the pain lessens if one does not shrink from the duty."

"How can it be a duty to remember?" asked Sebastian.

"I think it is all part of the purging," said Lucilla. "That hard deliberate remembering of good leaves no room for the remembrance of evil. That way we hasten the time. Don't you sometimes think, Mr. Weber, that one of the dreadful discoveries that we shall make in the life to come will be the extent to which we have put the clock back, and kept humanity upon the rack, by the mere unwilled thinking of idle moments?"

"The mind has pits," murmured Sebastian. "You have to be in a moderate state of normality to control your mind, Lady Eliot. A haunted mind, a sick mind, or even a mind weakened and bewildered by a sick body, hangs always over a pit of darkness."

He was aware of something very odd happening between them. She remained sitting regally upright beside him for a moment, and then she got up, helping herself with her stick. The rose she was wearing fell out of her belt and lay at his feet. "Let it stay there," she said when he bent to pick it up. "It's where I should be. It's where I am. Old age imagines itself wise and experienced. I'm sure I don't know why. One knows no more about how it feels to be wet through if one sits watching the storm from inside a warm room for one hour or one minute."

He picked up the rose, but it was full blown and the petals fell. Holding them in his hand he got up and faced her. "I am glad that the room from which you have watched the storm has been sheltered," he said. "We need warm people; they distil the sun. And even in a warm room there can be pain. And I think old age is wise. Taught by long watching, you feel your way from the lesser pain to the greater, and bear something of that, too, and that is sympathy. The actual storm sometimes blinds the eyes, but sympathy can be very clear-sighted."

Absent-mindedly he put the rose-petals in his pocket, and as they crossed the little bridge together he smiled to himself, thinking how ridiculous their conversation would have sounded to an eavesdropper: almost like an interchange of civilities between two grandees of old Castile. Yet for him it had been a refreshment because in this old lady, as in Mrs. Wilkes, he was aware of a well of quiet; this time the quiet not so much of acceptance as of unshakeable faith.

"I envy you your faith," he said to her.

"It is a special gift to age," she told him. "When the symbols grow dim they are replaced by a new sort of certainty of things to come."

She had answered the question he had asked himself, and he dared to probe her further. "The dead return?" he asked her.

"They are where they always were," said Lucilla. "Only you know it."

"I had wondered," he said.

PRIOR HUGH

IN fearing that they faced disintegration without him men had forgotten the momentum that men of genius leave behind them in their works. The life of the monastery moved on in the course he had appointed for it for several centuries, the only major change being that a succeeding Abbot became the first Bishop of a newly formed fen diocese, the monastery church his Cathedral, and the Prior of the monastery became its head. During these years the church was beautified in many ways and the Lightfoot clock, and the statue of Michael the Archangel, were placed high in the Rollo tower. Bishops and Priors came and went and some were saints and some were not, and some were beloved in their day and some were hated, but none was remembered excepting only Prior Hugh, who was Prior at the time of the dissolution of the monasteries.

He was a little man, quiet and peace-loving, so that men were not surprised when they heard that he had commanded his monks to yield humbly to the command of the King's Grace, and to offer no resistance when the commissioners came to drive them from their home. Yet when they arrived, with a formidable array of armed men as escort, and on a cold snowy day rode up the hill to the monastery to take possession of it in the King's name, it was found that the Prior had schooled his monks for a departure of dignity and grandeur. He himself in his simple monk's habit came out from the Cathedral and stood in front of the west door, at the top of the flight of stone steps that led up to it, and it seemed to the towns-folk and peasants who had come crowding and weeping up the steep streets to see the last of the monks who had looked after them for so many years, that he was a much taller man than they re-membered. His voice, as he cried out to the commissioners and their men to stand aside that his sons might pass out, had an authority in its tones that none had heard before. Then the great door of the monastery, that opened upon the wide greensward that stretched from the front of the steps to the Porta, swung open and the monks came out in procession singing with splendid vigour the fighting psalm, the sixty-eighth, "Let God arise and let his enemies be scattered." Their great gold processional cross, and their banner of Michael the Archangel, were forfeit to the King, but at their head walked the youngest novice carrying a large cross made of two bits of wood nailed together. As they passed beneath the foot of the steps their Prior raised his hand and blessed them, and he kept his hand raised until the last of them had passed out through the Porta. They could be heard singing as they went down the narrow cobbled street that led to the North Gate, and across the bridge over the river to the rough road beyond that led back through the fen to the world they had renounced. Their singing died away and what happened to them no man ever knew, though for centuries afterwards it was said that on nights of wind and driving snow the chanting of the monks could be heard sounding through the storm.

When the last of his sons had disappeared the Prior dropped the hand he had raised in blessing and turned and walked back into the Cathedral. They found him later lying dead before the altar, the knife with which he had ended his earthly life lying beside him. It was not the action of a true priest, who may not himself dismiss from life the soul that is God's, but it was an act for which men nevertheless remembered him with sympathy and admiration. Even his enemies were grieved and defying the law that those who take their own life must not be buried in consecrated ground they buried him where they had found him, laying over his coffin a flat black stone such as covered the body of Abbot William. No man afterwards dared disturb his bones, and for years it was remembered that some poor half-crazed girl had vowed that on the day of his death she had seen two swans flying over the city towards the setting sun, and their wings were of pure gold. And so these two men, the first Abbot and the last Prior, lay the one behind the high altar and the other in front of it. Four centuries divided them but in the life of the great Cathedral that was no more than the exhalation of a breath.

THE CHOSEN CLOCK

THE DEAN had taken off his hat and was standing before the clock. "I need not trouble Job," he said quietly. "There is only one clock in the world that I want to give to my wife."

"I am glad, sir," said Isaac. "When you have put up the shutters, Job, you may come back. I must tell you, sir, that I had Job's help in making this clock. He was of great assistance to me."

"That increases the clock's value," said the Dean.

Job went out to the street and put up the shutters in a state of great bewilderment. What ever had made Isaac part with the clock? It was to the Dean, of course. Yet he had thought that Isaac would have cut the heart out of his body sooner than part with the clock. The shutters in place he came back to the workshop and stood in the shadows behind the two old men, who were talking in low voices of the glory of the clock. It *was* a glorious clock. It seemed to Job that until this moment he had not himself realized what a masterpiece had been achieved. It stood illumined by the lamplight, shining out against the shadows behind it as sometimes the setting sun is illumined against the dusk. The golden fret that hid the bell was the loveliest Isaac had ever made. The two swans were just rising from the reeds, one with wings fully spread, the other with his pinions half unfolded. Job could understand from experience, and the Dean through intuition, what an achievement it had been to form those great wings and curved necks into a pattern that was a fitting one for a clock fret and yet alive, but only Isaac knew how he had laboured and sweated over it. This had been a costing clock. Yet the figures of the signs of the zodiac were as fresh and lively as though they had stepped with ease to the clock face. The ram, the bull, the heavenly twins, the crab, the lion, the scales, the scorpion, the archer, the sea goat and the man with the watering pot were bright as their own stars, gay as the little figures in an illuminated manuscript. But the virgin and the fish had something more than life and gaiety.

"She stands in her blue robe at her own hour of vespers, full of the peace of that hour," said the Dean. "Expectancy too. A great expectancy. Only six hours to midnight."

Isaac was startled. He had intended no Christian symbolism when he had painted his virgin in a blue robe. He had chosen blue merely to balance the blue of the watering pot at nine o'clock and the blue fillet that bound the archer's head at three o'clock. But the pretty Christmas story was a part of him and had obtruded itself.

"Six hours to midnight," repeated the Dean. "There you have combined the two symbols very excellently, Mr. Peabody. The fish, the ancient Christian symbol of Christ our Lord, and the Sun of Righteousness, the Light of the World."

With a pang of something remarkably like jealousy Mr. Peabody realized that the Dean's homage, that he had seen through the window, had not been entirely for his clock, if for his clock at all. And what had he been thinking of to put only one fish at twelve o'clock? Pisces, the sign of the zodiac, had two fish. He could only suppose that out of the deeps of his memory that one fish had come swimming up into the light, to remind him now suddenly of his father. For it was his father who had told him how the martyrs had painted that fish on the walls of the catacombs, and traced it in the dust that one Christian might recognize another.

A SHILLING FOR THE GAS

AFTER Miss Brown had left him Jo Isaacson put away his violin, poised his battered hat with something of an air upon his bony head, and strode off through the hot streets in the direction of his lodging, walking with the loping dogged stride of those who always walk because they cannot afford to do anything else. And as he walked he looked now and then at the shilling in his hand. He had gone out that morning with the express purpose of earning a shilling so that he might have the wherewithal to end his life with the assistance of the shilling-in-the-slot gas fire in his room. But he had not expected to earn the shilling so quickly and easily. Shillings were damned hard to come by these days.

It was Jo Isaacson's creed that a man's life is his own and that he has a perfect right to do with it what he will; if he wishes to end it that's his affair and no one else's. There had been many occasions in earlier days when he had been near to ending it, but yet had always been held back by the strange hope that he always had, the hope of the artist in pursuit of beauty, the hope that there was going to be something incredibly lovely round the next corner . . . a refuge in the wood . . . something . . . some sort of rest . . . some sort of abiding place.

But that morning he had awakened with hope dead within him and fear gripping him like a vice. The war had taken an appalling turn and his pessimistic mind saw no hope for England. The Jews would be hounded out of this country as they had been hounded out of all the others. He would once more have to make the choice between flight and persecution and it was a choice that he felt he could not make again. He was too tired to make a fresh start, too weak to suffer further.

And this morning he had also faced the knowledge that so far as he could see he was no longer of the slightest use to a single human creature. He had been of some use lately as nursemaid, court jester and fiddler-in-ordinary to his landlady's small daughters Moppet and Poppet, but today they were to be evacuated to the country, they would be gone when he got home, and there would be quite literally no one in his life who needed him. His existence would be an empty show. Nature abhorred a vacuum and so did he. If she would not smash the hollow empty thing that was his life, then he would. So he had come out to try to earn a shilling for that gas fire.

Well, here was the shilling lying on the palm of his hand, but with it had come the knowledge that his music still had power to move another human creature. That fact was to him almost incredible. With his worn-out talent and his worn-out violin he had not believed such a thing possible. Yet it had happened. In deadly fear himself he had yet by his playing made fear more bearable for another. The force that in the old days of his fame he had so often felt burning in him as he came forward to the footlights on the concert platform, careless how much it scorched him up if it could only use him as an instrument of strength for others, that fire that for want of a better name he had called life, had used him again. He was still an instrument. The fact was so astounding that he could scarcely take it in. His confused mind groped about feebly, seeking for its implications, realizing that it had somehow changed the current of his life, yet unaware yet what action he must take because this thing had happened.

What were those words of Flecker's that he had half remembered when that woman asked him about the pilgrimage? He had not thought of them for years but he remembered them now.

But you are nothing but a pack of Jews

.   .   .

Sir, even dogs have daylight, and we pay.

.   .   .

175

But who are ye in rags and rotten shoes,
You dirty-bearded, blocking up the way?

. . .

We are the Pilgrims, Master; we shall go
 Always a little further: it may be
Beyond that last blue mountain barred with snow,
 Across that angry or that glimmering sea.

White on a throne or guarded in a cave
 There lives a prophet who can understand
Why men were born; but surely we are brave
 Who take the Golden Road to Samarkand.

Well, that was almost always the choice of his race; to go on. Brave, yes, but were they not damn fools? Was there anything at the end of the pilgrimage? It was his belief that there was nothing there.

But he hoped he had not let his mockery show too clearly when that little woman made her trite remark about "beyond the veil". What a revolting phrase! But it was a very popular one and he hoped he had not smirched it for her, for women often clung to clichés when they had nothing else to cling to. She had been a pretty woman, too quiet-looking for most people's taste, but undeniably pretty. He'd always liked pretty women. His love of beauty and his constitutional dread of loneliness had led him to have intimate relations with a good many, only to find to his bitter disillusionment that none of them was what he had thought she was going to be; they all went stale sooner or later. But that woman had had a freshness that was the very antithesis of staleness, and she had seemed to fling her whole soul into the look of compassion she had given him. Quite a charming thing, that look of hers, to be one of one's last memories on earth.

But here his fumbling thoughts came up again against that incredible fact that life had used him, and it did not fit somehow with the fact of suicide.

Yet he told himself that the circumstances of his life were not altered because his playing had that morning pleased one unknown woman. She had been an uncritical creature, and the miracle was not likely to occur again. Moppet and Poppet, who had needed him, were still gone from his life. The future was still a thing that he could not face.

God, how he hated the loneliness of perpetual wandering! No satisfactory companionship was possible if you could not strike down roots. It had been partly the fear of loneliness that had made him choose music for a profession, for music is such a companionable thing. But his talent had been insufficient to make a great musician of him. In spite of his Leipzig training and his early successes his talent had been insufficient. You can't manufacture talent. Hard work can lay hold upon many things, but it cannot lay hold upon the gift of genius. Youthful fire and charm and vigour and passionate devotion to his art had seemed to do as well in the early days; they had made him a capable violinist and later first violin in a famous orchestra; and later still, for a short while, something of a celebrity. Then they had seemed to peter out, and the plodding doggedness, helped on by a good bit of drinking, that took their place had not been nearly such a good substitute. He had played in theatre orchestras, and then in cinema orchestras, and then in the streets. He had fled in turn from Germany, Austria and Italy. He had been moved on until he was sick of being moved on, and now he was fifty-five years old and until this morning's shilling nothing but coppers had come his way for weeks.

How was it possible to go on living under such conditions? God, how his music had lied to him in the old days when it had seemed to promise so much! Side by side with his love of it had come lately a sort of hatred. It was a beautiful but lying jade. It promised what it could not give. The Andante of the Ninth, for instance, what right had that damned lying fool Beethoven to write such a thing! That outpouring of sorrow, that deep grief, interspersed with those strange trumpet calls, then the heavenly melody breaking through the grief and lifting, lifting, triumphantly mounting upon untiring wings—where to? Nowhere. That final hymn in praise of freedom and brotherhood brought him no conviction.

The thing ended and the lights went out and you were back in the slime where you'd always been.

He caught his shabby old coat on some barbed wire and cursed angrily. Every reminder of the war made Mr. Isaacson feel sick. Barbed wire entanglements in the streets of London, gun emplacements at street corners, barrage balloons in the sky, men in uniform, women in uniform, all dressed up as smartly as you please simply to kill and be killed in a hopeless struggle. "There'll always be an England", they were singing in the pubs and whistling on the streets, and would soon be hollering in the shelters when the bombs were falling. But Mr. Isaacson doubted it. In his opinion the bleeding Germans had won this bleeding war and soon, if he did not make sensible use of that shilling, he would see in the streets of London what he had already seen in the streets of Vienna . . . Jews shamefully maltreated . . . No wonder that woman had flung him that look of pity.

A sudden blind insensate fury seized him. Pity! Pity! If it was not persecution it was pity. Pity was a damned insult. What right had she to pity him? She was perhaps one of those fools who believed in something or other, who was ready like all the other fools to suffer and die for abstract ideas that disappeared into nowhere the moment you came up with them, for hopes that were never fulfilled and lights that went out; but that gave her no right to pity him. Well, let them believe their fairy tales if they wanted to. It did him no harm. Only let them refrain from insulting him with their pity who in his acceptance of negation had now attained to the final wisdom and the final courage.

"If in this life only we have hope, we are of all men most miserable."

The clear voice halted him abruptly. Was it that woman speaking? He looked around him a little wildly, but there was no one. He had had no breakfast, the perspiration stood out on his forehead and his hands were shaking. Am I light-headed he wondered? Then he saw the words scrawled in white chalk on a blank wall; and his fury turned to rage that he had been so taken in. It was some fool in the district who went about every night with his bit of chalk ornamenting harmless walls with sentimental clap-trap from his

Bible. Such fellows were public nuisances and should be dealt with accordingly. Mr. Isaacson swore and went on.

But his confused thoughts were fumbling now not only with that incredible fact that life had used him, but with the everlasting tormenting question as to the nature of life and the extent of the hope that might be entertained of it. "If . . . if . . ." It had tormented Hamlet, and rightly, for it was the only question. For if life were the immense thing that that fool with the chalk maintained, then one would not dare to break any instrument that it saw fit to use. One would not dare. One would wait in patience till life itself did the breaking.

TRANQUILLITY

ISAAC FINDS SANCTUARY

ISAAC crept up the steps to the Cathedral like a fly slowly ascending a vast wall. The cold weather was over, and though it was still only February it was almost warm and the sun shone from a sky like blue silk. But the bright day was not making it any easier for Isaac for it only intensified by contrast the darkness of the Porch of the Angels. It looked like the threshold of a great pit. It was here that long ago he had stopped short and fought with his father rather than go in. But he had to come this way because if he had gone in through the south door he would have got involved in conversation with old Tom Hochicorn, who might have wanted to go in with him. He was not acquainted with the bedesman of the west door, who in any case sat inside and not outside and could be more easily avoided. For this was something he had to do alone. Yesterday Mr. Havelock had given him the Dean's watch, and with it a piece of paper on which Mrs. Ayscough had written, "I leave to my friend Isaac Peabody my watch and my faith in God." Now Job had Isaac's old watch, and the Dean's, attached to its fine gold chain, was ticking quietly within Isaac's waistcoat pocket. And so he had had to do what the Dean had so often wanted him to do, and come to the Cathedral. It was too late, for the Dean was dead, but all the same he had to do it even though the Dean would never know.

He plunged into the darkness of the porch, stumbled through it and fumbled at the great iron-bound door. It had a handle but in his fear he did not see it. He had never acquired the adult and saving grace of standing aside from himself and laughing at his own absurdities. Like a child, the experience of each moment absorbed him far too intensely for him to be able to look at it. He was in a panic now because the great door would not yield when he pushed it, and he beat on it with his fists. It was opened quietly from within by the bedesman, and he passed in.

The splendour seemed to fall upon him like a vast weight, but the door had closed behind him and he could not go back. He began to creep up the nave, seeing nothing, for after the first glance he had kept his eyes on the ground. He saw only the ancient paving stones, worn into hills and valleys by the tread of many feet. They were stained with colour because the midday sun was shining through the south windows. Veering sideways like a crab he nearly collided with a pillar, its girth greater than that of any tree he had ever seen. To steady himself he leaned his hand against it. The stone felt rough and somehow friendly under his hand and he noticed that just beyond the pillar there was a wooden bench. He let go of the pillar and went to it and sat down, his head on his chest and his hands between his knees. He noticed that the colour that lay upon the paving stones was lapping over his old cracked boots. Now and then a small cloud passed over the sun and it faded but a moment later it was back again. His breathing grew a little easier and his sight cleared.

Beyond the toes of his boots was another of the big old paving stones and then a flat black marble slab let into the floor. Words were cut upon it, "God is the Lord by whom we escape death," and above that the name of his friend, and the date, and that he had been Dean. The colour was lying on the dark slab just as it was lying on Isaac's boots. Just that, he thought, only that. He liked the simplicity but he could not understand why they had put those words. The Dean had not escaped death. His grave was under that stone.

He did not move on any further, for he was tired, and still he did not look up, but he began to feel less frightened. The pillar and the bench and the humble grave patterned with colour began to take on a look of familiarity. Beyond the small sunlit patch was the terror of the Cathedral, but here there was homeliness. And something more. He had been bitterly cold when he climbed up the steps to the porch, but now he was glowing with warmth. He felt as though someone had wrapt him about with a comfortable old coat, yet the glow was within him too and about it he wrapped himself. He had experienced something of the sort so many times before in his good times, but not quite like this. Before he had not known what the warmth was but now he did know.

He took the beautiful watch out of his pocket and looked at it, holding it cradled in both hands. He looked at the monogram A.A. and on the other side of the pair cases the words from the sixty-eighth psalm, "Thy God hath sent forth strength for thee", encircling the mailed hand holding the sword. He remembered the watchcock inside, with the little man carrying the burden on his back, and the wreath of flowers within the hour ring. And this watch was his. Whatever had made the Dean take such a fancy to him, a cowardly, selfish, obstinate, ugly old fellow like him? He would never understand it. He took the piece of paper out of his pocket and looked at that too. Faith in God. God. A word he had always refused. But the Dean had said, put the word love in its place. He did just that, speaking to this warmth. "Bring us, O Love, at our last awakening, into the house and gate of heaven." The words had slipped as gently into his mind as the colour came and went over his boots. Just lately so many things that the Dean had said to him were coming back to his memory. He had scarcely attended to them at the time but they must have sunk down below the surface of his mind to its deeps, because now they were slowly being given back to him. Sentence by sentence he quietly remembered the whole prayer. Though it said, "at our last awakening", he felt himself to be already in the house. It wasn't any different anywhere else to what it was here. If he moved on through the Cathedral all of it would be as homely as it was here because of this warmth, and when the house lights went up the great darkness would be full of friendly faces.

He put his watch and the piece of paper back in his pocket, got up and went out into the centre of the nave. He walked back a little way towards the west door, and then stopped. There it was, the other Michael clock. It was just as it had been described to him. Above the beautiful gilded clock face, with winged angels in the spandrels, was a canopied platform. To one side of it Michael in gold armour sat his white horse, his lance in rest and his visor down. On the other side the dragon's head, blue and green with a crimson forked tongue, rose wickedly from a heap of scaly coils. The stillness of both figures was ominous. They waited only for the striking of the bell to have at each other. It was a wonderful bit of work. The tip of Isaac's nose glowed rosily, so happy was he in contemplation of this clock. And to think that he had lived in the city all these years and had not seen it! To think he had lived here for nearly a lifetime and never come inside the Cathedral. Fool that he had been! Slowly he turned his back on the clock and looked down the length of the Cathedral. For a moment he ducked his head and gasped, as though a wave had crashed over him, and then he went steadily on down the nave.

For an hour he wandered round the Cathedral. Once, far away, he heard the clock strike twelve, and knew that Michael was fighting the dragon. The splendour, the vastness and the beauty no longer terrified him, though they made him feel like an ant. For he was at home. He was not able to take in very much today but he would come again and learn this glory by heart, like a man turning over the leaves of some grand old painted book. But the Dean would not be with him to turn the leaves. He thought this, and suddenly the tears started to his eyes. A few trickled down his cheeks and he fished in the tail pocket of his old coat for his scarlet spotted handkerchief. He blew his nose and was startled by the noise it made in the great silence of the place. It was not fitting. Tears were not fitting. He put his handkerchief away and looked about him.

He was in a small enclosed place like a chapel, where a lady lay upon her tomb. Close to the tomb was a plain stone altar and beside it a recess in the wall, like a cupboard, though the door was no longer there. Over it was a small beautifully carved arch. Though he did not know what it was it appealed instantly to the craftsman of small things that he was himself and he walked over to it. He had never heard of an aumbry but he thought to himself that some holy thing had once been housed here. It was a house, the Cathedral in miniature. He touched the tracery of the small arch with his fingers, delighting in it, and then without realizing what he was doing he put his right hand inside the recess, and found that the roof of the tiny place was a carved replica of the great ribbed roof of the choir. With his heart pounding with excitement he slipped his fingers along the delicate curved flutings, like the convolutions of a sea-shell. They were hidden away here in the darkness where no one could see them. Here was this loveliness, and his craftsman's fingers could read the beauty as the eyes of a musician read a score of music, and it was hidden. But the treasure within had known of it. Love, that had made it, had known. None else.

"The watchcock, Mr. Peabody."

He stood where he was without moving. He had heard the Dean's voice, though not with his ears. Yet he had never heard anything more clearly. There was a chair near him and presently he moved to it and sat down. Yes, that is how it is, he thought. He had known it when he had sat on the bench by the pillar. Love was vast and eternal as this great fane appeared to his sight, yet so small that he could possess it hiddenly, as once the cupboard in the wall had housed its treasure. He did possess it. When his good times lifted him to the place of safety he was always in love with something. The love of Adam Ayscough was not dead but at every step that he had taken within the Cathedral had accompanied him. Love, and nothing else, was eternal. "Love is the Lord by whom we escape death."

He sat and thought of his father and he no longer hated him. "Now I shall get to know him better," he said. "And I'll get to know Emma." He sat for a long time and thought to himself that he wished he knew how to pray, yet he knew, untaught, how by abandonment of himself to let the quietness take hold of him. Then he got up and wandered away, and found a door and went through it. Outside, sitting on a stone bench by a small glowing brazier, was old Tom Hochicorn.

"Good day, Isaac," said Tom. "Been in there long?"

Far up above their heads Michael struck his bell. Isaac took out the Dean's watch and verified the fact that Michael was correct in recording the hour as one o'clock. "About an hour, Tom," he said.

Tom Hochicorn's eyes twinkled with amusement. He said, "So it's got you, eh? I allus thought it would."

OASIS OF PEACE

SOMEHOW they battled through, they never quite knew why
or how. It was as though they had entered into a whirlwind
and after hideous battling had found themselves standing
serenely in the core of peace at its centre. Rachell learnt the lesson of
withdrawal into her own innermost tranquillity, André learnt that
monotonous toil can be so used that it becomes the rhythm of
thought, the pulsing background of the accompaniment that sets
the notes of the violin winging to height beyond height. And both
of them learnt that peace that is not threatened has no value, and
thought that is not bought by pain no depth.

. . .

After dinner Rachell went up to her bedroom. She always went
away by herself for a little at this time and woe betide anyone who
dared to disturb her. She guarded this little oasis of peace in her
busy day fiercely and jealously. At other times of the day work and
servants and children were claiming her, and at night she was her
husband's. This was the only time when she belonged to herself
alone . . . Sometimes she felt that these few moments kept her
sane. Her family thought that she lay down on her bed and rested,
but she did not always do this. Sometimes she prayed, sometimes
she read a little, but more often she sat quite still with her hands
lying in her lap and her eyes closed. Sometimes she would murmur
to herself as she sat, "Underneath you are the everlasting arms,"
and then she would feel her spirit sinking down and down through
depths of tranquil light, that grew cooler and sweeter the further
she sank, until she felt herself resting serenely against something,
drawing in strength and peace through every fibre of her being.
This lovely experience did not come to her always. It had come to
her first one day when she had been in great physical pain that had
almost wrenched her body and soul apart . . . She had been
frightened that first time and thought she had been dying. "It was

as though my soul had come loose," she said to André afterwards. It came to her now whenever her life was very rigorously disciplined. At the slightest hint of self-indulgence, even in thought, it took wings and fled from her. Only ceaseless struggle could keep it with her; but she struggled; life without it was like a desert without wells.

BY ROMANY FIRELIGHT

YOBEN took off his own cloak and put it round Madona's shoulders, for she had nothing to keep her warm but the tattered remnants of an old red shawl, and at their backs the night was growing chill. She raised her arm, with that protective gesture he knew so well, and lifted the cloak about his shoulders also. It had been made for him in the days when his body had been more adequately covered with flesh than it was now, and with Madona a wraith there was room for both. She laughed happily, and pointed to the glowing fir-cones. "Fire flowers," she said. "Nothing more fair to see." He smiled, watching them a moment where they lay in their glowing nest, each bract delicately outlined in golden fire. About them licked small tongues of flame, blue and crocus-coloured. No, there was nothing more fair to see, unless it was the night sky above them; or Madona's face in the glow of the flames.

Madona Heron was eighty years old and had a face of transmuted tragedy. Ten years ago it had expressed only the nobility of selfless endurance, but now it expressed also peace and delight. For nearly a lifetime she had endured without complaint every sort of ill-treatment from her husband Piramus, a man of violent temper and cunning cruelty, she had borne many children and mourned the deaths of most of them, she had put up with cold and exhaustion, near-starvation, persecution, in a perpetual cycle, and taken it all as merely her lot. And now her long patience had brought her at last to the point where the sense of personal struggle ceases for a soul and she is passive and at rest in other keeping than her own.

Madona lived now as though lifted above life. Piramus no longer ill-treated her because he got no kick out of it; she was detached as a cloud in the sky. As she never considered herself at all, she was unaware of what had happened to her; she only knew that life was good. Yet she did not, like so many old people, cling to life, because she clung to nothing. Yoben, understanding where she stood, rejoiced in her joy. It was so seldom that a soul lived long enough in this world to attain such heights in a body that allowed her to enjoy her peace. For, say what men would who had never so suffered, detachment from severe physical pain was impossible unless the body died under the torture. It was when the iron touched your own flesh—your flesh—he wrenched his mind back to Madona. She had never ailed more than a little. Her black eyes were still clear and bright, and though she was as frail as a brown autumn leaf she held herself upright and still moved with ease. Her face was very thin and the fine bones showed clearly through the wrinkled skin, the firelight glinting on the outlines of the high cheekbones, aquiline nose and square chin and showing pits of shadow about the sunken eyes and in the hollowed cheeks . . .

Madona turned her face up to the sky and the diklo fell back from her straggling white hair. Her lips parted and the outlines of her face softened as she smiled. She adored the moon. She gloried in all the works of God, but in making the moon she thought He had surpassed Himself. One of the things she enjoyed about Yoben was that he listened when she talked of the moon. The other men did not. To them it was no more than a useful light to go poaching by. Only Yoben agreed with her that moonrise was a lovelier thing even than dayspring, and that it was natural that the old should wish to live long enough to see just once more that silver light pouring from the sky.

"Nearing the full," said Madona, "and the weather set fair. Night after night now she'll show us the dearie things of earth, the fields fashioned of light and the trees from darkness; we'll not lose them."

THE SECRET GARDEN

THERE was another garden at Damerosehay besides the flower garden and the kitchen garden, and that was the wild garden, which lay to the west of the flower garden, the kitchen garden being on the north and the oak-wood on the south. It had originally been the part of the flower garden where the oak-trees grew and Lucilla had made it by erecting another brick wall to divide them, and moving one of the beautiful wrought-iron gateways with which Damerosehay abounded from the kitchen garden to give access from one to the other. The wall was almost hidden now by the mind-your-own-business which tossed its sprays like white foam over it, and the gate was hidden by a great bush of guelder-roses, so that the wild garden was very secret indeed. Lucilla had wanted to keep some reminder of the Damerosehay that she had seen on that first spring morning, that overgrown place where she had dreamed of the blue bird and David had seen it, and so she had simply left the wild garden more or less alone to go mad as it liked. The grown-ups thought Lucilla was as crazy as the garden, but the children blessed her foresight every day of their lives.

Especially Caroline. When she was here, with the boys at their lessons and the grown-ups busy over their mysterious employments, she knew that she would be quite alone, undisturbed by anyone except Jill bringing her her eleven o'clock milk and biscuits, and she liked Jill so much that she hardly counted as a separate person.

Clasping Gladys, and smiling at David where he sat beneath the ilex-tree, she ran through the tame garden, slipped behind the guelder-rose bush, and lifted the latch of the gate that led to the wild garden. It latched behind her and she gave a deep sigh of content and stood still for a minute to survey her kingdom.

The oak-trees in the wild garden, sheltered by the wall and by their brothers in the wood, were less wind-blown and stunted than those outside. Their branches were less twisted and more graciously spread, their foliage thicker and their hoary lichened trunks stouter and straighter. They were less like battle-scarred warriors and more like wise and mellowed councillors, set there not for defence but for encouragement and support.

And certainly the other growing things in the wild garden took every advantage of the encouragement offered. Traveller's joy grew everywhere. The honeysuckle raced up the oak-trees and in summer blew its trumpets victoriously at the very top, the mermaid rose, that hardy rambler that will go anywhere and catch hold of anything, clambered along the branches and sent festoons of creamy golden-hearted blossoms to sway in the wind beneath them like fairy swings. As for the mind-your-own-business, sadly restrained by Margaret as it was on the flower garden side of the wall, it let itself go completely on the wild side. It leapt exultantly off the wall and hung in thick curtains of ivory blossom that swept the moss-grown path and even encroached upon the rough grass beyond.

All the loveliest wild flowers grew in this grass in their seasons, primroses about the tree trunks in April, bluebells in May, ragged robins in June and daisies at all times. There were still garden flowers running riot here, michaelmas daisies, hollyhocks and Japanese anemones, lavender and rosemary, for Obadiah was allowed in now and then to scythe the grass and keep the brambles down so that they should not be choked completely out of existence. But there was never any suggestion of real cultivation in the wild garden, it was just a glorious natural wilderness of colour and scent.

And how the birds loved it! They seemed scared of the twisted oak-trees beyond the wall, but these beneficent creatures inside were their friends, and the whole garden was their sanctuary. The children put food here for them in winter and Tucker was severely chastised if she dared to come in over the wall. Even the dogs were discouraged, in case they should bark at the birds and frighten them. The blackbird, at such times as he was not singing in the ilex-tree, was singing in the wild garden, and on the very top of the tallest tree a big missel thrush was for ever crying out to the world that God is good. A robin lived here too, a bullfinch and a chaffinch, and the wives of these creatures, every kind of tit and wagtail, called by Jill "Polly-dishwashers", willow-wrens, hedge-sparrows and tree-creepers. On rare occasions a goldfinch was seen flashing his splendour through the trees, and a couple of exquisite rose-breasted red-starts fluttered over the bushes, so fragile that they seemed each of them more like a gasp of wonder than a bird. Only the sea birds never came here. They knew better. It was not their province. Once a sabine's gull had tried to take refuge in the wild garden from a violent storm, but all the other birds had risen up in a cloud of fury and attacked him with savage beaks and raucous cries and he had fled back to the comparative kindness of the wind on the marshes.

Spring, when the birds were nesting and the bluebells were budding, was the best time in the wild garden, but autumn could be lovely too. As Caroline stood gazing the Japanese anemones were like fallen moons beyond the grey trunks of the oak-trees and there was a soft mist of mauve where the autumn crocuses were growing in the rough grass. The fires of autumn had already touched the leaves over her head, and spun from twig to twig and from bush to bush was that exquisite silver filigree of dewy spiders' webs. Caroline went slowly forward along the path that led in and out through the tree trunks to the secret centre of the garden where Methuselah was.

He was the oldest of the oak-trees, taller and larger and hoarier than any. It was on his topmost branch that the missel thrush sang and among his leaves that the willow wrens nested. In spring the loveliest primroses grew about his gnarled old roots, and in autumn the autumn crocuses grew here thicker than anywhere else.

When Lucilla had first come to Damerosehay she had found the remains of a battered swing hanging from the stoutest of Methuse-lah's branches, showing that once a child had played here. She had taken it away and put a new one for David, and as the years went by an even stouter one to sustain the weight of Stephen's children, and then a very strong one indeed to carry the sometimes combined weight of Ben, Tommy and Caroline. It was a perfect place to have a swing, for here you were as secret and safe as though shut in the heart of a flower. No one could see you and you saw nothing except leaves and birds' wings, flowers and grasses. No one visited you except the sunbeams or a silver shower of rain, and, sometimes, the lady and the little boy.

Caroline, like David in his boyhood, was a lonely child. Except for Lucilla and her adored Jill she thought but little of the human race, and Grandmother and Jill were so often busy about other things that she did not see a great deal of them. Not that she minded. She liked solitude, especially in the wild garden. Yet like many solitaries she felt the need for some sort of companionship, even if it was only a companionship of her own creation. Talking to oneself palled, but Caroline found that if one shut one's eyes and just talked, not to oneself but to someone unknown outside oneself, when one opened one's eyes that someone was there . . . And she thought the person really was there. She forgot, if she had ever realized, that her own wish had had creative power . . . That was how she had got to know the lady and the little boy.

It had happened first last year, when Mother had been staying with them, on an autumn day like this one, when she had been feeling particularly forlorn. She had eaten all the sugar out of the nursery cupboard and there had been a good deal of unpleasantness with Ellen, from which she had fled to the shelter of Methuselah's kind arms. Sitting in the swing with the slow tears oozing out from under her shut lids she had felt the urgent need to tell somebody about it, and so she had just begun to tell.

"I was *not* greedy," she had said. "It was because Mother said I was a skinny little shrimp, and I thought that if I got fatter she might love me as much as she loves the boys and so I ate the sugar. Then Ellen scolded and Mother said I was a greedy little pig, and I couldn't tell her why I had eaten the sugar because if I had I would have cried, and Mother doesn't like cry-babies."

At the end of this recitation she had opened her eyes and at first she had thought that all the autumn crocuses that were growing about her feet had flown up into the air like a cloud of butterflies, because there was a sort of mauve mist before her eyes, but when she looked again she saw that it was a lady in a mauve dress, with a lovely full skirt that swept over the grass like a wave of the sea.

At first Caroline had thought this lady was Mother, because she was tall and dark and slender like Mother, but when she looked again she saw that she wasn't really a bit like Nadine. Her face was rounder and softer and her eyes shone in a way that told Caroline without any words that she, unlike Nadine, liked little girls every bit as much as little boys, and that she quite understood about the sugar. And then a funny little boy dressed in green, with red curls and a head far too large for his body, had popped out from behind the lady's skirts and grinned at Caroline, and Caroline had wriggled out of the swing and run to him, and they had played in the garden together all the morning, and the lady had sat on the grass and laughed.

Thinking it over afterwards Caroline could not remember what they had said to each other, if indeed they had said anything. But they had been blissfully happy. This mother had not been so much a mother, as the mother, the mother of everything in the garden, of herself and the little boy and the flowers and birds and everything. Though she was dressed in mauve instead of in blue, and wasn't really a bit like her, yet she had somehow reminded Caroline of the picture of the Madonna that hung in the nursery. But her name wasn't Mary. Caroline knew quite well it wasn't Mary, though she didn't know what it was.

And as for the funny little boy, well, he was the perfect companion, that companion of whom we all of us dream under so many disguises, the outward form altering as the years go on, but yet seem somehow never to find.

So often since that day Caroline had seen them, though only in the wild garden; indeed it sometimes seemed as though she could make them come at will simply by shutting her eyes and talking to them. She knew, as she trotted along to the swing with Gladys, that she was going to see them today ... And she did.

When Jill brought her out her milk and biscuits at eleven she was sitting in the swing, very demure and bright-eyed and rather more rosy than usual.

"Funny little thing that you are!" exclaimed Jill. "Happy all alone?"

Caroline took her mug of milk and buried her nose in it. She vouchsafed no remarks but her eyes twinkled at Jill over the top. She could not tell even dear Jill about the lady and the little boy, but she could let her share her joy.

Jill sat down on the grass beside Caroline with a sigh of relief. It was a joy to escape from Ellen's perpetual harrying and be alone with Caroline for a little while in this lovely secret place. And mercifully Caroline was always a very long time absorbing her milk and biscuits, for she liked food and she always made it last as long as possible. Jill sat very still, with Gladys in the crook of her arm, and lifted her face, her eyes closed, to the warm sunbeams that struck down through the branches of the oak-tree. She could hear the flutter of wings near her, and birdsong and the murmur of the sea, and her free hand, pressed down hard upon the earth, lifted itself unconsciously to caress the cool grass and the crocuses and the rough sun-warmed bark of the tree. "Well," she ejaculated suddenly, "it would not be so bad to be blind, after all. The sound and feel of things is that nice."

Caroline gulped down the last of her milk, removed her countenance from her mug and looked at Jill a little anxiously. Jill was talking to herself and she was rather afraid that when she opened her eyes she might see the lady and the little boy.

Yet all she said when she opened her eyes was, "Wipe your mouth, lovey. You've milk all round it."

Caroline took a microscopic handkerchief from up her knickers and wiped her mouth with relief. Somehow she did not want even Jill to know the secrets of this secret garden.

Jill got up with reluctance. This old tree, with the patch of flower-jewelled turf around it and the trees and bushes closing it in on every side always made her feel so safe. Had she been able to express what she felt she would have said that it was the inner sanctuary of the Damerosehay garden, as the drawing-room with the carved overmantel was the heart of the house. It seemed that in both of them the best of all that had ever been at Damerosehay was very safely kept. From them its life's blood flowed out. She picked up Caroline's mug and went away very slowly. It was always hard to leave the wild garden.

When Jill had gone the little boy came out from behind the tree trunk and Caroline played with him for a long time, while the lady sat in the swing, her mauve skirt billowing out over the crocuses, and laughed. And then suddenly they were not there, and Caroline wondered why until she heard a clear whistling in the garden, like the blackbird but yet not the blackbird. It was David's whistle that he always used to tell the children that he was coming.

NEAR TO DEATH

"I N the old days spring was spring and summer was summer, winter was winter and behaved accordingly. Now the seasons are in as great confusion as the world, with spring warmth in December and snow in May. It never did that in the old days."

"You're laughing at me," said Lucilla, without pique.

"No, no!" declared Sebastian, in dismay at the mere idea.

"You may not have realized it, but you were," said Lucilla. "With indulgent affection for me, I'm glad to say, just as my children do. I know the look in the eyes. I am so glad you can laugh at me now. When you first came you were like Queen Victoria."

"Queen Victoria?"

"You were not amused," said Lucilla. "Did you ever see Queen Victoria?"

"No, Lady Eliot, I can't say I did," said Sebastian, and this time he laughed outright. "You see, I was not born when she died."

Lucilla looked at him. "You are laughing, but I am not," she said. "You should be thankful I am not the sort of woman who cries, or the arithmetic I am doing would have me weeping. It is not as one of my children that I should be thinking of you, but as one of my grandchildren."

"Provided you count me among your family that's all that matters," he said, his usually hard, dry voice suddenly warm with delight of the fact that he could love her, a fact that gave him much greater delight than the fact that she could care for him. With his amusement a spark of brightness struggling for existence in his usually lightless eyes, he looked round and saw the burning curiosity in hers only partly veiled by their compassion. He hastened to relieve the curiosity. "I am forty-eight," he said.

"You look sixty," she said. "I didn't probe, did I?"

"You never probe," he said. "None of you do. I am in peace among you all, and at Damerosehay. To leave you will be infinite distress."

"Then why do it?" asked Lucilla. "Were you thinking of leaving us?"

"Mr. Eliot's secretaries come and go. I can hardly have the good fortune to stay here till I die, can I?" he asked her, smiling.

"It depends how long you take about dying," said Lucilla. "Are you wanting to die?" she continued serenely.

"Yes," said Sebastian. "I should like to be finished with it now."

"So should I," confided Lucilla. "Though I don't say so to the children, for they would be hurt by my wanting to leave them. Except to my son, Hilary, of course, who agrees with me that I can love them just as well there as here, if not better, and that it's natural at ninety-one I should have got very tired of dressing and undressing my body. Because, you know, at ninety-one that's about all one does. By the time you've got rested from dressing it's time to undress."

"You're not speaking the strict truth, are you?" said Sebastian quickly.

"No," said Lucilla, after a moment's pause. "I am not. I am fond of dressing and undressing, for I like clothes. And that's not all I do. I pray. I take trips in Hilary's car on fine days like today. I worry. I talk a great deal, and very sententiously, as you well know. Thank you for reminding me."

"Ah, but I was not reminding you," he said in distress. "I was grateful for all you said to me that evening among the rushes. I spoke without thinking. It was just that —"

"I know," said Lucilla. "As one comes near to death strict truth seems to matter more and more. It's the awful justice that waits for us that makes us feel that way. I said I wanted to die. I do almost always, but not quite always. Sometimes I feel the terror of death. The soul shrinks from justice and the body from dissolution."

"That's justice, too," said Sebastian. "What else does this body deserve? It has been the garment of our selfishness."

"Yes," said Lucilla. "But I have looked sometimes at the bodies of those I love and thought I saw an immortal stamp upon them."

"So have I," said Sebastian. "A look or a smile. Something. But the stamp is not the wax. Yet it's good to get the stamp by heart, for it will make the new body of selflessness recognizable." He paused and smiled. "I talk as if I know. How can I know? We know nothing. It's just an idea that came to me this afternoon."

TRUTH

THE LITTLE THINGS

"I WANT to tell you, Edith. Today is the first time I have been in Ash Lane. Well, I've been busy, so perhaps I'm not to be blamed for that, but I am to be blamed that I walked through the door as though I'd done so every day for weeks. I wanted you to think I had. I deceived you and deception is stealing because it takes away the truth. Forgive me, Edith."

Edith was looking away from her. Could a child understand such a very feminine bit of vanity, of compunction? Suddenly Edith jumped up and came to her, flinging herself into her arms and sobbing wildly. She held the child but in utter bewilderment. What had she said to provoke this primordial grief? It seemed vast and hopeless, like Eve's in the garden when she knew what she had done. She asked no questions but waited and presently Edith stopped sobbing and was silent.

"What is it, Edith?" she asked at last.

"I stole them," whispered Edith.

"You what?"

"Stole them."

"What did you steal?"

"Queen Mab in her coach and the little blue tea-set."

"Tell me about it," said Mary.

"When the old lady was ill I used to go and kneel in the conservatory and look at the little things. I pretended they were mine; especially Queen Mab and the blue glass tea-set. And then one day Mother said the old lady had sold her oak chest. And that night I had a nightmare, and the next morning I went to see if the little things were there. They were still there and the window was open." She stopped and began to sob again.

"And so you took Queen Mab and the tea-set to keep them safe from being sold like the chest," said Mary. "If I had been you, and nine years old, that's just what I should have done."

Edith looked up at her astonished and speechless, her face red and blotchy with her tears, the most bedraggled-looking child Mary had ever seen. "Yes, I should. It was unthinkable that Queen Mab and the tea-set should go away to some dusty shop in a town. They'd have died there. When I was your age my Cousin Mary, that's the old lady, offered to give them to me. But I wouldn't have them. I lived in London and I couldn't take them from the green parlour to London."

"Then you don't think I'm awfully wicked?" whispered Edith. "You don't think I'll go to hell?"

Mary laughed. "No, I don't. It's like this, Edith. Why you do a thing is more important than what you do. And so stealing because you love is really better than not stealing because you don't. Not that I am advocating stealing exactly. This question of good and evil is very complicated. Life has been very difficult for us all since Eve ate the apple. Let's wash your face with the well water. I'll lean over and dip my hankie in. Where are Queen Mab and the tea-set now?"

"In a box inside my handkerchief case. I'm always frightened that Mother will find them and ask questions. You're quite sure I shan't go to hell?"

"Quite sure. What will you do with them now?"

"Bring them with me when I come to lessons tomorrow and put them back again with the other little things. And I'll share them with Rose and Jeremy if you want me to."

The depth of her own relief astonished Mary. "That's a good girl! Now it's over and you haven't got to think of it again."

Edith cried again in sheer relief, and then let Mary bathe her face. Then they laughed together, each aware of the buoyant lightness, as though a tangled string had snapped and they floated free.

SQUIRE HASLEWOOD'S LETTER

"REVEREND Sir, I must tell you, sir, that God has had much mercy upon me, granting me a great enlightenment of the spirit. After Edgehill fight I was in much despondency, but He led me to strength and comfort. He led me to a man as great as any I have known, to a Joshua among the Lord's people, to Colonel Oliver Cromwell, of whom if you have heard any evil you will know it is a lie put about by the devil himself. Through him I was led to the Lord's chosen, to that sect called the Independents, to whom alone the Lord has revealed His will in these troublous times, who are a chosen instrument unto Him for the delivery of this unhappy country from an evil and popish tyranny. Sir, I have found strength and peace and a courage not my own. Sir (I say it with all humility, for the glory is the Lord's), I stood my ground at Brentford. I owe to the Lord much service and this I would perform. Zeal for the Lord consumes me. I would have the Lord's house, where you serve and where I worship, a place purged of idolatry. I command you in the name of the Lord that the painted panels in the screen, and those heathen images which you have set about the church for its defilement, be removed and burned. And I command you, once more, as I have commanded you before, that the Lord's table be placed where it should be, in the centre of the church, and that the cross upon it be removed and taken to the manor. The matter of the melting down of it for a purpose pleasing in the eyes of the Lord I will attend to when I come. I forbid you to use the Book of Common Prayer. It is the devil's book. Henceforth you will not patter and mutter like the priests of the great whore but pray as the spirit moves you, and preach the word of God and minister to the people in a plain black gown. Sir, I remain your faithful friend and servant, Robert Haslewood."

Parson Hawthyn sat for a few moments gazing at the dying fire. Then he pulled himself to his feet, gathered his old cloak about him, and with the letter crumpled up in one fist went out into the sunshine, which he did not see, and crossed the churchyard to the church. In his accustomed spidery corner he fell to his knees and prayed that he might be able to pray. His prayer was not, he thought, answered. Nothing was given to him but desolation. He sat back on the bench behind him, the crumpled letter upon his knees. He looked at it stupidly for a while and then thoughts began to form slowly in his mind. That Robert had suffered a conversion, that he had in truth had an enlightenment of the spirit, he did not doubt. The letter was sincere. He believed that Robert had indeed found the strength that God alone can give, and for that he gave thanks. He was no bigot. He believed that truth is a great globe and that men see only that part of it upon which for them the light shines. He believed that through any creed held in sincerity the finger of God can reach and touch a man. He believed that if men struggled to find the light, they would reach the light, not only in spite of but through their mistakes and limitations. But there was one way in which they would not find it, and that was by turning back on the path upon which for them the light shone and taking another man's path for the sake of expediency or peace. He recalled the words of Sir Thomas More. "I never intend (God being my good lord) to pin my soul at another man's back, not even the best man that I know." That to him was the sin against the Holy Spirit. That was loss of integrity, the way down into darkness, and he was not going to take it.

He raised his head and looked about him. The slanting sunbeams touched the small carved figures that he had made. In themselves they were of no importance. The birds and the angels he had made only to teach the children to praise God for creation, to teach them the care that the angels had for them. Our Lady in her niche and the saints in the screen were only painted wood. Even the cross upon the altar, the symbol of man's redemption, was a symbol and no more. Were the altar taken from the window of the morning and placed in the centre of the church he would stand there as Aaron. If his surplice was taken from him he could still say, "Come, people; Aaron's dressed," for he was a priest whatever he wore. If he used other words than those of the Book of Common Prayer he would still be praying. It was not that. It was that the ritual of the

Church of England was her ritual. To forsake it was to forsake her, and the Church of England was for him the path upon which the light shone.

He got up and with a heart full of dread, and at the same time full of peace, went out into the churchyard. Standing in the lane outside his cottage he realized again that it was a beautiful day. The sun was free of the mist now, and the melting hoar frost had strung every twig with orbs of light.

JOHN REFLECTS

JOHN agreed with Mrs. Wilmot that it was ridiculous to make such a fetish of housework as Daphne did. What did a little dust more or less matter? The communing of one soul with another was really more important, even if it were only on the subject of mice.

He thought to himself now that it did not much matter, in itself, what one did. It was chiefly as the vehicle of love or the symbol of prayer that action was important. Or did he only think that because in action he was himself generally such a bungler? Perhaps, if he faced the truth, he would find that one of the reasons why he spent so much time in prayer was because the results of prayer were unknown and one could indulge in the sin of wishful thinking. For it most certainly was sin for a man to sit back picturing the pleasing results of his prayer. Unless prayer was bread cast upon the waters in blind faith, without hope or desire for knowledge or reward, then it was nothing more than a selfish and dangerous indulgence of fantasy. It is difficult, he thought, for any human being to face the fact that he is really quite superfluous. He is always trying to find a loophole somewhere.

FRONIGA and Yoben rode home in a more leisurely manner than they had come, for it would be a night of moon and stars and they would see their way clearly even when night had fallen. And on this homeward journey they talked more, Froniga telling Yoben stories of her wild and happy childhood with her father and mother, of the years with Robert's parents, unhappy ones because Robert's mother had disliked her, and of her escape into freedom again. "It was my father who taught me the spells of a white witch that my mother had known," she said. "Always they must be handed on from man to woman and from woman to man. To whom shall I teach my spells, Yoben? To you?"

She looked at him, laughing, and saw a comical look of dismay pass over his face. Then he smiled and said a little stiltedly, "I am much older than you, Froniga. You must teach them to a younger man, or let them die with you."

"You think it would be better to let them die with me."

"I do not presume to judge you, Froniga. I have never concerned myself with what you believe, or what you do or have done. I have been concerned only in loving what you are."

"And that has contented you?" she asked.

"Yes, it has contented me. But I am a man, and a man rather ignorant of women. I have known few women well, and I have loved only yourself and Madona. I think I have perhaps been mistaken in judging you by myself. What has contented me has not necessarily contented you. The times are dangerous, Froniga, and if I should die in this war I shall leave you with very little knowledge of me. You will perhaps grieve that you have so little. Would you like to know more?"

"Only if you would like to tell me more," said Froniga.

"Up till now you have respected as well as loved me," said Yoben. "If I tell you more of myself, then you will be left only with your love."

"No," said Froniga, "for I respect the man I know today, in this present time in which we are together, not the man who lived in a past that I did not share. If it will ease you for me to share it, I shall be glad, but only if it will ease you."

It would ease him, Yoben thought. He had been thinking of this sharing only for her sake, but now he wanted it increasingly for his own. This long day together, bringing them nearer to each other than they had ever been, had seemed to lift their love on to a new plane, almost into a clearer atmosphere. He had never been less conscious of her as a woman, and for that very reason had never been more conscious of her as a companion, in the sense of unity upon the same timeless journey. He realized that human love, if it is to last beyond death and approximate a fraction nearer to the divine, must feed on truth. "Froniga," he said, "by silence I have deceived you. I have only just realized that."

"Don't reproach yourself. Deception that you conceived to be your duty has become second nature to you, has it not?"

"You're right. A recusant priest. A Royalist spy. I have never been able to be anything openly. You could pull off my disguises like the skins of an onion and always find another underneath. And the core rotten—fit only to be thrown away."

"And not yours either to judge or to throw away," said Froniga. "Only our disguises are our own. Tell me about yours, Yoben. I never thought you were a gypsy. I have learnt lately that you are a spy. After that night last autumn when I angered you so with my careless speech I wondered if you had, perhaps, Papist sympathies. As to the other—of that I had no knowledge at all."

Her voice was quiet, but her face was turned away from him. He tried not to think of what her feelings might be, this Puritan woman who would have been brought up to fear the very name of Papist, but to think only of what he must say. "I am English," he said, "and was born in England. My parents died when I was still young and I was sent to the Spanish Netherlands, where my father's brother was a Jesuit priest at the English College at Douai. There I was rigorously trained as one of those missionary priests sent across the Channel year by year to keep the Catholic faith alive in England. I was an ardent and rather passionate boy, but not as physically strong or as morally courageous as I imagined myself to be. Somehow that hard discipline of the seminary, that tempered so many proud spirits, did not teach me humility. When the time came for me to leave with other priests for England I had no doubt at all about my own powers of endurance, even to the point of martyrdom. I was more than ready, I was eager, for the martyr's crown of roses and lilies. I had not laid to heart the wise words of Sir Thomas More, who would not press upon martyrdom 'lest God for my presumption might suffer me to fall'. It was a strange existence that we had in England, Froniga. We were not there to convert Protestants to the faith, and we did not try to proselytise; we were there, in the words of our mandate, for 'the preservation and augmentation of the faith of the Catholics in England'. And we had to do it hiddenly, for there was no protection for Catholics in the old Queen's days, or in the days of King James; to be caught hearing or saying Mass meant fines and imprisonment for the laity and torture and death for the priest. We lived sometimes under grim conditions of hunger and cold and poverty. It was a hard life, always with its undercurrent of ceaseless danger. After a few years it told upon me and I fell ill. I think that in my fever I must have spoken of the hidden things, for the first time I went abroad again after my illness, to say Mass in a certain Catholic house where the faithful had gathered on Easter morning, they came and found us. My congregation escaped, but I was caught."

"Do not go on, Yoben," said Froniga sharply. "I cannot bear it."

"Am I not riding beside you safe and sound?" he asked bitterly. "And do you suppose I should be so crass as to harrow your feelings with details of physical torture?"

"I should not mind if you did. What I cannot bear is to look upon a man's shame."

"You will not look on mine. It is too deeply buried. The few plain facts that lie above it I can recite as drily as a chandler pattering the price of corn, for I know them so well and have lived with them so long. I and another priest, a frail old man who later died in prison, were taken to London. For the last bit of the way we were pinioned on our horses, our arms behind our backs and our legs fastened together under the horses' bellies, and the people in the street pelted us with rubbish. We were imprisoned in the Tower, but not together. I was alone in a filthy dark little cell, so small that I could scarcely stretch out in it. I was there for many weeks, each day expecting to be put to the torture. I became ill again, and as I waited for it day by day and week by week I came to have a fearful dread of the torture. I was afraid I should fail. Yet when it came at last, and I was on the rack, I did not fail. I answered none of the questions the rack-master put to me. I was carried back to my cell and left for ten days and then, with my limbs still crippled from the first torture, I was racked again, and this time I was promised my life, and the means to leave England, if I would give the information that was asked of me. But again I kept silence and this time, though the pain was so bitter, I felt some of my old presumptuous self-confidence returning. I realized that my courage was equal to it. I could do it. I was the victor, not they. I came back to consciousness, that second time, still with that sense of confidence, and found that I was not back in my cell but still there in the torture chamber. The rack-master bent over me, asking me the everlasting questions all over again, but gently and with tenderness, praising my courage and promising me peace. It would be a pity, they said, to put me back upon the rack. And it was then, not on the rack at all but lying on my back on the floor, that I broke down completely and told them all I knew. I even told them of matters that had been confided to me under the seal of confession. They kept their word and set me free and I left England, but because of what I had told them, several good men were ruined and imprisoned and my three closest friends died the traitor's death at Tyburn. And you know, Froniga, what that death is."

There was no sound but that of their ponies' feet on the road, and the birds singing. Froniga did not speak, for she could not. For a few moments she felt the pain that the man beside her had endured for so many years . . . Withered and dry, a branch broken from the tree, burnt up with fiery misery . . . She had often been allowed to share the suffering of others for a few moments, but she had never shared anything like this. It passed abruptly, as such things did.

"How old were you, Yoben?" she asked at last.

"Twenty-five."

"What did you do?"

"Not the one thing I should have done—return to Douai and submit to whatever discipline was judged best for me. I was too much of a coward for that and perhaps still too proud. My instinct was to disappear, sink away from the companionship of decent men, and I followed my instinct. I became a vagabond in Europe, picking a living as best I could."

"Yoben, do you not think that the fearful results of your failure made you believe that it was worse than it was? It was only your nerve that failed, not your will. It was weakness, not sin."

For the first time they looked at each other. The astonishment in his eyes turned to something almost like antagonism and she realized that the relentlessness that had gone into his training had become a part of his judgment of himself for ever. Nothing she could say could soften it now. "Never mind, Yoben," she said quickly. "I do not see this quite as you do. Never mind. It is long ago now. So you became a vagabond in Europe. Where did you become a gypsy?"

"In Spain," he said. "I had always been attracted by the gypsies and now they seemed akin to me, wandering for ever in expiation of their sin. I was with them for many years and then I found myself longing for the gentleness of England, the green springs and the golden fall of the leaf. I joined a ship's crew at Lisbon and sailed from there to Ireland, and from Ireland I got to Scotland, and then journeyed down through the great hills to Cumberland. There I fell in with Righteous Lee, Madona's brother, and came south with him."

"And would have given your life for him," said Froniga. "The Herons have told that story. The village know it and I know it. Did it grieve you that you were not allowed to die on the gallows for old Righteous?"

"Yes," said Yoben. "I had hoped to be allowed to suffer for another man something of what my friends had suffered for me. If we could choose our purgations, I suppose we would all of us choose to suffer as we have made others suffer, to feel every cruel word we have spoken enter our own hearts, to have withheld from ourselves what we have withheld from others. Yet that's partly pride, Froniga, the desire for that tit-for-tat that restores equality. The gift of free forgiveness would humble us more. In prison, nursing my disappointment and my sore ears, I saw that at last and managed to stop clutching hold of that hope. I gave it into the hands of God, to be or not to be as Heaven wills."

"How did you come to work for the King as you are doing?" asked Froniga.

"Both in Spain, and in England later, I always heard Mass when I could," said Yoben, "for I have never become so desperate as to try and cut myself off entirely from the mercy of God. In Catholic Spain I had been able to slip into a church among a crowd of peasants and not be noticed, but in England I could not do that. I had difficulty in finding the hidden congregations, and when I did find one the appearance of a Catholic gypsy among them was an alarming phenomenon. For the sake of their own safety they would question me and I would have to answer their questions. I became well known among them at last and it was known that I had been a priest. Before the war all the best officers in the King's army were Catholics and I came to know some of them well. When war became inevitable they thought I could be useful. Is there anything else that you would ask me, Froniga?"

"Only one thing. Have you never served as a priest again?"

"Only once. A priest was taken ill suddenly and I was asked to take his place. It seemed my duty, but it was a fearful thing to me."

Froniga would have asked him why it was a fearful thing and then something in the quality of the silence that had come between them stopped her. They rode on and gradually she understood why it was a fearful thing and felt a sudden sharp anger. If he thought their long self-denying love a sin, then she thought he was a fool, though she loved the fool no less for his folly. Hot words rose in her, but she did not speak them. They rode on for a long time in continuing silence and then by mutual consent drew their ponies to the side of the road, and forgot them. The ponies cropped the grass, and the man and the woman looked at each other.

From that long wordless look Froniga gained great knowledge of Yoben. She realized, as she had not done before, how utterly his love for her had flooded his haunted, lonely life. She had been like sunshine in cold and desolate places. She had transformed his life and he had not been able to give her up. Like the young ruler in the story, who could not part with his great possessions though his soul's life depended on it, she had been the one thing that he could not relinquish. He had yielded everything else, but not this warmth and sunshine, without which he had come to feel that he could not live. Yet looking with her far-seeing eyes deep into his spirit she saw how the weakness that had betrayed him before was betraying him again. He was not able to free himself from his enslavement to her. If she did not set him free he would die with his soul in chains. Yoben, meeting her steady, piercing glance, felt a sense of panic. His spirit wanted to recoil and creep away, to hide from her. It took all his courage to open himself to her gaze, yet not to do so was to cheat her. No good to stop short now, to reveal so much and no more. If she wanted full knowledge of him, she must have it even if it was his doom. He could not read her as she read him. He saw her face grow white and cold and it seemed that something of her beauty withered. He did not know how long they stayed there, or what sort of struggle was going on in her. The sunset had been golden when he had begun to talk to her, now it was dusk, with great moths flitting, and a silence of birds. He felt that life was draining away from them both, leaving desolation.

"It's cold," he said, and did not know he had spoken.

"We'll ride on," said Froniga.

They rode quickly now. Night came and the stars clustered thickly in the sky, and still they had not spoken to each other. Near home, in the hollow in the beech-wood where Yoben would have to turn aside to reach his camping place, they stopped. He dismounted and came and stood beside her bridle, his hand on hers, waiting for her to do what he had not the strength to accomplish for himself.

"Good-bye, Yoben," she said steadily. "I do not want to see you again. Since you knew me you have never been free to serve God with a single heart. Till the end of our lives we will long for each other, and the longing will seem more than we can bear at times, but I expect it is the one thing needful for us both, for if we do not one day find each other in God, we shall never find each other again at all."

He seemed rooted to the spot. His hand moved on hers, caressing it. "Don't, Yoben!" she said sharply. He kissed her hand, took his pony's bridle and went straight away into the darkness of the woods without looking back. She rode to the manor, stabled Baw and let herself into the dark house without knowing what she was doing. She went softly through the sleeping house to her room, undressed and got into the big four-poster bed. Unconsciously she pulled herself into the far corner of it, cowering away from the moonlight like a whipped dog. She lay with her knees drawn up, as though she were in pain, motionless for an hour or more. When she began to weep at last the sobs seemed tearing her to pieces like hands tearing a rotten sheet. The emptiness within her and all round her was appalling. She had said once to Yoben, in her ignorance and foolishness, that there are more ways than one of consummating love, and the hardest way can be the best. But she had not known it was like this. There was nothing grand or inspiring about renunciation. It was just all the years of your life stretching ahead in a long grey dreary emptiness. There was no comfort anywhere. The thought of death was too far off to bring any comfort, for she was physically so immensely strong. She would live long. If the hours were so leaden, what would the years be? They would never pass.

Yet a tract of time did pass and she could no longer refuse the compelling light. For hours it had been drenching her while she lay with her face buried in her hands. She turned over in the bed and stretched out her cramped limbs. Their aching, the discomfort of her nightshift drenched with sweat, of her face stiff and sore with weeping, seemed somehow to ease the other pain. She was aware of the moon, remembered vaguely the old story, and the loneliness of sun and moon. Her sore eyes could not bear the brightness and she shut them, but her body seemed soaking up the light and presently she slept.

WHEN TO SPEAK OUT

"Mothers understand mothers." The girl beside her shivered, but, like a good surgeon, she went inexorably on with the job. "Were you thinking about your little girl just now?"

"She had a toy swan," said Annie-Laurie, her eyes fixed now on the beautiful creature on the water in front of her. "She took it everywhere. It got awfully battered."

"Had she? Caroline had a frightful old rag doll with a patch on its nose. She wouldn't look at anything else. I believe she's got it still. I've never lost a child, but I can imagine how all the little things would stab one till the end of time."

"Especially when it's your fault," said Annie-Laurie.

"You mean you blame yourself because your baby died?"

"Yes. She had bronchitis. I went out one night to do my work—I thought I ought to—I'd our living to get; for Luke, my husband, was too ill to work at that time. He said he'd look after her. But I ought not to have gone. She wasn't fit to be left. It was a cold night, and he opened the window bang on her."

There was a pause, and then Nadine quietly asked a question:

"Deliberately?"

"Yes."

For two days Nadine had been thinking over the story that Hilary had told her, wondering about many things, but in particular what it was that had turned Annie-Laurie's love for Luke to hatred. Something, of course, to do with the baby. She had guessed before this that the child was the crux of it all. She looked round, and saw Annie-Laurie's eyes fixed on hers with blank horror. That brief yes had been surprised out of her by Nadine's quietness. She would have given the earth to have withdrawn it.

"Annie-Laurie, now that you've told me that much I think it

would help you if you told me everything. Was your husband very ill? If so perhaps he was not in a normal state of mind when he opened the window."

"No, he wasn't. And he was insanely jealous, too, of my baby's father—of Jim. And of Midge because she was Jim's child. We'd longed for a baby, Luke and I, but we had not had one."

"Try to tell me everything, Annie-Laurie, as you would have told your mother. Try not to leave anything out. It is never fair to anyone to tell a half-truth. It is a form of lying, and it confuses judgment."

If Annie-Laurie had hesitated, she did not after that. All her life she had taken her stand on truth. Bit by bit, bravely, she told it all, while Nadine listened patiently, fitting among the facts she already knew those that until now Annie-Laurie had told no one. Given those facts there was no more confusion in the story.

Though Annie-Laurie had been in an anguish of fury over the open window, though she had bitterly reproached Luke for it, she had not suspected him of more than gross carelessness until the evening of his death, when he had himself told her that he had exposed Midge deliberately. They had had a row over Malony, and he had not cared what he said if only he could hurt her enough.

"He had suffered so much that he was not sane," she kept saying to Nadine. "He was not to blame. He did not know what he did or said. And it had been an awful shock to him, after we had loved each other so much, to come back and find me married to another man. I could not make him understand how I felt about Jim. I never loved him as I loved Luke—I never shall—but I felt safe with him. I was grateful to him, and he needed me. It was awful, that evening he told me he had—almost—murdered Midge. It threw me right off my balance. After that, I was hardly sane either. I cried out, 'I hate you, Luke. I hate you so much I'd like to kill you,' and I cried out so loudly that the people in the next flat heard me."

But she had not meant to bring back the wrong tablets from the chemist. Malony's explanation of her conduct then had been the right one. It was not until Luke was actually taking the first one that she saw her mistake and then, deliberately—as deliberately as

217

Luke himself when he opened the window upon Midge—she held her peace and let him take the second. She had not known, of course, what it was that he was taking; for all she knew it was something harmless. But she had not bothered to find out. When she had found him deeply asleep, she still had not bothered.

"It was as though what he had told me had been a blow on the head," she said to Nadine. "I was stunned. I didn't come to myself till the next morning. So, you see, that verdict of not guilty was a wrong one. I killed Luke."

She had told it at last, the thing that had poisoned her life and nearly disordered her reason. Her straight back sagged, and she seemed to shrink in upon herself, as though she had no more strength left in her.

"I'm sure I'd have done the same," said Nadine quickly. "I believe any mother would."

After that she sat quietly beside Annie-Laurie, not touching her, but willing that the warmth of her understanding might reach to her. "Defend us from all adversities which may happen to the body and from all evil thoughts which may assault and hurt the soul," she had prayed once in her room at the Herb of Grace, that first time Annie-Laurie had talked to her. The old inn gave one a very comforting feeling of physical protection, but this wood gave one more than that: a sense of spiritual safety, of release from the burden of tormenting thought . . . There grew in it the hellebore, that was for the healing of mental sickness . . . After a while Annie-Laurie straightened herself, and with both hands pushed the hair back from her forehead with a gesture of such unutterable relief that Nadine knew she was released. She had told at last.

"I ought to have told at the trial," said Annie-Laurie. "But I was afraid of what they might do to me. I'm a coward, you know. I've always been afraid of things—I don't know why. But I tried not to tell lies. I didn't think then—what you said just now—that to tell only half the truth is a form of lying. Perhaps—do you think—I ought to tell Jim?"

"Yes, I think you ought. I think he deserves that you should not keep anything from him. Why did you not tell him before? Were you afraid you would lose his love?"

"No. I don't think anything I could do would make him love me less—he's like that. It was for Luke's sake I did not tell. He would have asked me how I had come to hate Luke so much. I did not want him to know what Luke had done to Midge. You see, I had loved Luke and—you'll think this odd—after he was dead I loved him again."

"Yes, I can understand that. Death has a way of wiping out hatred. And it does more than that: it increases understanding. It's queer, but after people are dead you find that you understand them better. There's a poem that says, 'What the dead have no speech for, when living, they can tell you, being dead.' Perhaps that's true. I don't know. But I think you'll find, when you tell Malony what Luke did to Midge, that he won't hate him for it. He'll understand quite well that he did not understand what he was doing . . . Annie-Laurie, why haven't you remarried Malony and had another child?"

She knew, but she wanted Annie-Laurie to tell her, and Annie-Laurie told her.

"I promised Luke I wouldn't. Once, when he was very ill one night and thought he might die, he made me promise. I tried not to, and then I had to, just to keep him quiet. After he was dead because of—what I'd done—I felt I had to keep that promise. It was the only reparation I could make."

"That was a promise for which Luke had no right to ask, and you have no right to keep."

"I have to keep my word," said Annie-Laurie stubbornly. "You were talking only a little while ago about the importance of truth."

"It's difficult," said Nadine gently. "In my own life I've found decisions about truth almost the hardest to make. When to speak out and when to hold one's peace. Whether it is best to hurt someone with the truth or make them happy with a lie. It's dreadfully difficult. Generally I think it's a question of charity. Those who are leaving the world have no right to impose their will upon those they leave behind them; that's a sort of seeking after power that's deadly selfish. And no one has the right to seek ease of conscience at the expense of another's happiness; that's selfish, too." Nadine pushed her fingers up into her hair with a despairing gesture. She

219

hated doing it. Hilary ought to have been doing it. Mean of him to have put it on her. But love for Annie-Laurie drove her on. "Even though you are together, yet you can see from Malony's face that he's a most unhappy man. He wants proper married life—children and a home. You've no right, just because keeping your promise to Luke eases your misery of remorse, to keep Malony on the rack."

"You see," said Annie-Laurie slowly, "it's Luke I really love."

Nadine looked at her. So that was the likeness between them. Annie-Laurie couldn't let go of Luke, any more than she had been able to let go of David. She had gone with Malony, even as Nadine had gone with George, but not with a single mind.

"Let your love die," she said sharply, almost savagely. "Cut it right out, like a cancer. Cut the whole past right out. Try your hardest to forget it. People with divided allegiance are crazily unhappy, and make others unhappy. Let it be Malony, and Malony only, with what he stands for, now and until the end."

Annie-Laurie wrung her hands in an unconscious gesture of wretchedness.

"It would be like killing Luke over again."

"Nonsense! That's sheer sentimentality. When I said 'Let your love die,' I meant die out of your conscious mind, out of the part of you that has to deal with daily living here and now. It will live on in the innermost part of you, of course. Everything we've had and been does that. Perhaps in some way we find it all again after this life. I don't know. I only know that here and now, today, the happiness of those we live with is what matters. I've no right to talk, Annie-Laurie. I haven't practised what I preach. But I'll try—if you will."

MARGUERITE TAKES THE VEIL

EVEN the most well-trained minds are guilty occasionally of the most ridiculous and lamentable wanderings at the most unsuitable moments. Next day, as she knelt with the other novices in the Chapel of Notre Dame du Castel, clothed in the black serge gown and the white linen wimple, the holy habit of religion that would be hers now until she died, with the sweet high voices of the nuns rising about her in the Kyrie eleison, she opened her eyes suddenly and saw a mouse run across the chapel floor. It was an exceptionally comic mouse, with a very long tail, and Marguerite, at this most solemn moment of her whole life, had to cover her face with her hands to extinguish an irrepressible giggle. And then, thick and fast, her girlhood's memories came tumbling about her. It was a stormy day, and the rushing mighty wind that was sweeping in from the sea beyond the convent walls, the tumult of it almost drowning the chanting of the nuns, took her back easily to another stormy day, and the wind was banging the door of the Le Paradis garden shut behind her and Marianne, and she was running over the cobbles of Green Dolphin Street and chasing her brown beaver bonnet with the pink ribbons up the narrow passage of the Ozanne's house. And then she was running into the doctor's arms, and he was picking her up and carrying her into the parlour, and there was William in his gay mad green clothes standing laughing in front of the fire. And then she was sewing her sampler in the parlour, with William's mouse hidden in the folds of her dress, and then she was weeping stormily because Marianne and William had had some wonderful adventure together and had not taken her. And then she was racing over the sands with William, climbing with him up the slippery sides of Le Petit Aiguillon, holding out her arms to him at the top. Then she was La Môme, crowned with the chaplet of flowers, and William was lifting her to her feet and kissing her beneath the canopy of pink and white lilies. And then, the last memory of all, she stood beside William on the *Orion*, her hand trembling in his, and heard the quiet water murmuring against the ship's hull and the harp-thrumming of the breeze in the rigging over her head, and knew that from ages past she had loved this man and would for ever continue to love him. They were one flesh, one mind, one soul, a unity that nothing could divide, but just as William leaned towards her to tell her something there was an interruption and the words were never said . . . And now she was here, doing the banal, the melodramatic, the obvious thing that women had been doing for centuries, and renouncing the world because a man had renounced her . . . Only that was not the whole of it. By whatever devious and humiliating steps she had come to this place she had nevertheless come to the right place. Clothed in these austere garments, with the cold wind rushing by outside this old fastness of the spirit built high up among the clouds, facing a life of poverty, chastity and obedience, she was at home. A surge of joy went through her. If the wind was tearing the golden fruit off the trim little trees in their tidy pots it was with the perpetual sweep of its wings burnishing the stars. "Au nom de Dieu soit."

BEN'S DECISION

"DAMN fool," said John Adair, his red beard bristling with fury. "Rotten painter, are you? So you are. Rotten. So am I. So are most of us. The point is we *are* painters. Sit on your behind filling in forms at the F.O. if you want to. It's your affair, not mine. They'll pay you well. Your mother will be pleased. Pretty woman, your mother. I fell in love with her once, but I soon got over it. I never fell permanently in love with any-thing except painting. I had that much sense. No mothers or wives could ever take my mind off it for more than five minutes. What's that? Paint as a hobby? You young fool. If you say that again I'll knock you down. You remind me of a maiden aunt of mine. She painted roses in oils on velvet tea-cosies. Very pretty, they were. Well, it's a free country, as far as murder goes. Nothing to prevent you hitting the other fellow on the head with an umbrella if you want to. Murder Ben the painter if you wish. Rotten fellow, as you said. Well, I won't say any more, except that if you go to the F.O. I'll never speak to you again, and if you choose to paint I won't lift a finger to help you. You'll start from scratch, as I did. I don't say I won't lend you my old easel with the woodworm in it, and look at your work now and then and tell you how damn bad it is. And should you do a good bit of work, which isn't likely, I might talk about it, as I would about any young chap's work that appealed to me, but that's all I'll do. I won't use my influence to help you, and I won't lend you money. I didn't become the rich man I am (or would be, but for this damned income tax) by lending money to young fools. Let 'em starve, I say. Do 'em good. Now get out and think it over."

At that point he went to Lucilla for help, but she would not help. "No, darling," she said. "You must decide. I've advised people too much in the past. I've imposed my will on them too much. I don't do it any more . . . At least," she said, striving, as always in these days, after absolute truth, "I try not to do it any more."

And always there had been the pressure of his parents' deep anxiety. In a changing anxious world they wanted to see their sons safely settled in careers of financial and social security. They knew nothing at all about painters and their life, but they were quite sure struggling young artists could be certain of neither. They didn't know where their next penny was coming from and they consorted quite often with very odd people. Knowing Ben's weakness of health and of will, Nadine and George were worried to death. A life of financial uncertainty would bring back his asthma. Noisy parties in airless studios, drinking and smoking to all hours, would bring back his tendency to lung trouble. The very odd people would undermine his morals. He'd marry the wrong sort of girl. Meals at irregular hours would upset his digestion. From the moment of Ben's birth George had set his heart on his eldest son following him into his old regiment, and it had nearly broken his heart when Ben refused categorically to go into the army. But the Civil Service was the profession of a gentleman, according to George, and art was not. Of course when fellows painted the royal family and became royal academicians like John Adair, that was another story. But there was no likelihood of Ben being asked to paint the Queen, so far as George knew. George thought Ben's paintings were very pretty, but he couldn't see the promise of much eminence in them. Nadine said that even if there had been, Ben would never live to attain it. At this point, one day, she broke down and cried, and Ben, holding her in his arms and trying to comfort her, realized with a shock that this was the first time in his life that he'd seen his mother cry.

"See what you've done to your mother," said George.

It wasn't as though they were asking him to give up his painting altogether, Nadine and George both said pathetically, when Nadine was feeling a little better. He could paint as much as he liked over the week-ends. They liked him to paint. His sketches were very pretty and his portraits and miniatures charming, and the anatomy in his allegorical works had improved a great deal lately. But they didn't want him to make it his profession. At least, not at present. Of course in years to come, if he should really turn out to be a genius, the whole matter could be reconsidered again. But at present surely it wasn't too much to ask that he should at least give the F.O. a trial. Didn't Ben feel he owed something to his parents? Couldn't he do just this one thing to please them? And Ben said he would. Later he wavered again, but Nadine cried again, and he came back once more to the beginning of the circle.

"Thank heaven surgery is considered the profession of a gentleman," was Tommy's private comment to Ben. "But what rot it is! Poor old Pop, how he dates! Almost antediluvian. Kipling and so on. And Mother the same. She's a damn pretty woman, and she dresses well, and that makes her look less prehistoric than Pop, but in point of fact there's not much to choose between them. To all intents and purposes both of them might have been dead for years. It's odd how soon people date. David's starting to date now. Have you noticed?"

Ben said miserably that he hadn't. He longed for David, who had never confined his acting to week-ends, but David was in America.

"Badly," said Tommy. "And as for his acting, it's positively ham. It makes me squirm. I don't know how it is he still rakes in the dough. But look, Ben, I'm like Mother and Pop in this. Painting's all very well as a recreation, but it's a pretty poor show as a life's work unless you happen to be a genius, which, old boy, speaking quite frankly, I don't think you are. The painters one knows are so wet. They just drool around with locks of hair falling over their eyes. Of course if you're a commercial kind of chap you can make a bit by it, like old Adair, but you're not that sort. Not forceful. You're more the wet sort. Or at least you will be if you don't look out. You need to counteract that tendency. Better try the F.O. Don't take my remarks to heart, old boy. They are all for your own good."

Hilary, appealed to, was not much more helpful than Lucilla. "I know nothing about painting," he said. "I don't even know if your work is good or if it isn't. And even if I did know I should hesitate to advise you. The older I get the more chary do I become of giving advice, especially upon the matter of vocation, which lies between a man and his God. A true vocation is inspired, and if you deliberately refuse it, even for such good motives as love of parents and so on, you run the risk of spiritual disaster. There is a sin against the Holy Ghost which is not forgiven either in this world or the next, and the refusal of inspiration is a part of it. As to whether painting is your vocation, I don't know. Only you know. And if you don't know it's your business to find out."

"But how?" groaned Ben.

"For a start, leave off allowing your female relatives to make up your mind for you upon all the trivial matters of your life. Make up your own mind as to which tooth-paste you prefer. Try to get a little practice in decisiveness, indecisive fellow that you are. And in this non-trivial matter, go slow. The movement of events sometimes shows one the will of God. But once you honestly believe you've seen it, nothing in earth or hell should deflect you from it."

. . .

"You are very like your cousin," he said, as they walked up the paved path to the front door.

"Like David?"

"Yes."

Ben flushed with pleasure. "I only wish I were," he said. "He's a great chap. And he's succeeded."

"Is that so important?" asked Sebastian drily.

"I don't mean in that sort of way," said Ben hastily. "I mean, he's done the job he wanted to do as well as he could do it."

Sebastian noted the sudden hardening in Ben's voice, but he

only said, "Now I can see the old signboard. What are the blue flowers?"

"Rue, the herb of grace," said Ben. "The garden rue is yellow, but the wild rue is blue. It used to grow in these parts, but you hardly ever find it now. It's an astringent herb that's supposed to be good for clearing the sight—both sorts. Country people used to apply it for rheum and drink it to foresee the future. In our family we say it's the symbol of single-mindedness."

"A very good symbol," said Sebastian. "But I don't think I care for these hyphenated words of your complicated language. I prefer the single word integrity. The meaning, I think, is much the same?" He felt Ben stiffen beside him and went on easily, "But you've already expressed my meaning in describing your cousin. He's done the job he wanted to do as well as he could do it. You couldn't describe the integrity of the artist better. To others, perhaps, there seems a certain ruthlessness (or astringency) about the clear sight of the artist who has got rid of the rheum and fore-seen the future. He sees his job and his goal of perfection, and to hell with what gets in the light."

There was a sudden quiet but steely anger in his tone that astounded Ben. Sebastian had impressed him enormously, but, troubled as he was about his own affairs, he had not analysed the respect he felt for him. He had vaguely thought it the shamed admiration which the fortunate feel for those who have suffered ordeals which they are not at all sure they could have survived themselves. But now the sudden flash of the steel was so fierce that he felt transfixed by it. And in anger, too. He had thought the man liked him, but Sebastian's anger was hot in his body. He had thought of the poor chap as a broken man, but there was nothing broken about this steel, or the anger either. You can't break steel, nor fire. He opened the door, and as he waited courteously to let Sebastian pass in first, he dropped his eyes, that he might not see the contempt in Sebastian's. Then he was ashamed. He had accepted the thrust of the steel with an instant sense that this was justice. He must accept the contempt, too. Flushing to the roots of his hair, he forced himself to look at Sebastian. But there was nothing in the man's sombre lightless eyes but great kindness, and the gentleness of his face seemed almost to belie the anger. Yet the anger had been there, for the steel was still in Ben, stiffening him.

"Who told you?" he asked.

"I don't think anyone in particular," said Sebastian. "Just a word here and there. The way in which you have all so generously made me one of the family has made me know more about you all then perhaps I ought to know."

Ben was thankful for the astonishment that had made Sebastian suddenly forget all about him. He could stand beside him in the shadows and recover himself. The conversation had been of the briefest, and he supposed it had taken them only a few minutes to walk up the path and in at the door, yet it had seemed years. And nothing that John Adair, or Heliose, had said to him had shaken him like this. No, not shaken him, stiffened him, for he knew now what he had to do.

COURAGE

THE WILL TO DIE

RANULPH, as he ran up the lane and along the cliff with André, found himself confused in thought and feeling yet vividly aware of passing sensation. It was still raining and the sting of it against his face, and the wet cliff grass drenching him as he ran, made him feel as though he were already plunging through solid water . . . Water . . . Water . . . He would go back to the water . . . He remembered that moment of hideous pain when Rachell's eyes passed over him without seeing him. He no longer felt the pain, but he remembered it as a man remembers a signpost pointing him along his road. Feeling as he did, Bon Repos was no place for him . . . A swirling and rushing of wings was round them . . . Le Baie des Mouettes . . . He remembered Peronelle lying on the turf reading Browning, and his thoughts raced confusedly back to her and to the other children and their mother . . . He'd saved their home for them.

"Nearly there," panted André.

Ranulph turned for a moment and looked at him and André, meeting the look, smiled. They were locked once more into a moment of sudden and intense union . . . The one-time prisoner and the man who had set him free . . . What greater bond could there be between two men, thought Ranulph . . . Then the moment passed and he was only conscious again of the rain and soaking grass and his own laboured breathing.

The little path they were following swerved away from the sea and downhill, taking the curve of Breton Bay. A high hedge of blackberry bushes and sloe trees hid the bay from them but they could hear shouts from below. They plunged downwards, pushing their way through the bushes and grass, and slipping and slithering on the wet ledges of rock that thrust themselves up through the ground. The path reached the level of the bay and ended abruptly in a tumbled mass of seaweed-covered boulders. A landsman would have slipped and broken his leg at the first attempt at crossing those treacherous rocks, but André and Ranulph, Islanders both, leapt and clung like cats until they reached the firm sand of the bay.

A handful of fishermen, with Jacquemin, Hélier and Guilbert among them, were already dragging down their boats to the water's edge, but they were very few for the task in front of them and hailed the appearance of two more pairs of hands with a shout. Down on this lovely little curving bay there was hardly a stir of wind and the waves, with the tide going out, were negotiable, but outside the bay a huge sea was still running and Ranulph, looking at it, realized with exhilaration that they were all quite mad . . . The madness ran in his veins like fire and he could have shouted with delight. He remembered nothing but the excitement of the moment.

．　　　．　　　．

"Where?" he demanded of Guilbert as he took his place beside him and heaved at the boat with the rest.

"Les Barbées," said Guilbert briefly.

Ranulph looked out to sea, to the left of the bay. Fountains of spray now hid, now revealed, the rocks at the western edge of Les Barbées . . . Hideous rocks . . . Wedged between them he could dimly see a ship.

"Looks like a yacht," he muttered, "who on earth?"

"English," said Guilbert, and spat contemptuously.

"How do you know?" demanded Ranulph.

"Only the English sail yachts round the Island in spring weather," said Guilbert savagely, and spat again.

"Fools!" said Ranulph, but was grateful to them. Not for anything would he have missed this glorious exhilaration that was lifting him upon a peak of ecstasy. There was no more speech for they were off and every ounce of strength was needed for the oars. Even in the comparative calm of the bay it was hard work, and Ranulph wondered for a moment what it would be like when they were out beyond the sheltering cliffs. He soon knew. It was like being pitched suddenly into a mill race. The raging wilderness of water seized and caught them, and it took every ounce of strength in the bodies of the men manning the boats to keep their craft head-on to the wreck. Progress seemed impossible. "Hold her! Hold her!" Ranulph heard himself gasping, but his voice was lost in the rush of the waves and the screaming of the gulls. Then, as though by super-human strength, they held and steadied, and began slowly, slowly, inch by inch, to creep forward. The current was against them, and it seemed to Ranulph that with each straining effort unseen forces were pushing the boat back and back. He felt as though one moment's relaxation would send them hurtling backwards over an abyss. The spray was dashing over them, blinding and choking them but, thank God, the wind had dropped. To Ranulph, out of practice as he was, the effort of rowing was colossal. He wondered how André in another boat was faring, but remembered that André, though the weaker man of the two, was in better practice. Soon all sense of exhilaration was lost in the agony of his physical distress. A ton weight seemed fastened on the end of his oar, and with the effort of pulling it through, his lungs seemed bursting and every muscle in his body dragged out to torture point. The sound of the blood drumming in his ears seemed to drown even the sound of the waves. He could see nothing. A crimson curtain seemed let down in front of his eyes.

"All right going back," a voice seemed saying, "the current with us then. Just got to get there." Get there! But how to get there? How to endure long enough? The drumming in his ears turned to a roaring and his body seemed tearing into little pieces. It seemed to go on for a hundred years. At every stroke it seemed as though the breaking point were reached, and yet at every stroke his will thrust it a little further on—a stroke further on . . . A shout tore across his consciousness . . . They were there . . . Guilbert, the best seaman in the Island, who knew the surface of the sea as a palmist reads an outstretched hand, had brought them round to the far side of the wreck, out of the current. Ranulph, conscious that the others could now hold her, fell forward over his oar and the red curtain in front of his eyes turned black. A hand dragging at his shoulder roused him again. He looked up and saw the yacht looming up through the spray . . . There were those fools to get off her . . . Only a handful, thank God . . . He could see them up there, a few blue-clad sailors, a woman with a child, and a man clothed in what had once been white ducks. Obviously the imbecile owner. Guilbert was on his feet and throwing a rope. Ranulph tried to get up, but found he could not. Damn! His usefulness was over. Well, he'd helped to get them there. He could see André on his feet grappling with a rope in one of the other boats. André had weathered the gruelling passage better than he—obviously more strength in the man than he had thought.

The rescue of the yacht's crew was arduous. The waves were still boiling so wildly round the wreck that it was impossible to come near to her. The Island men could only fling ropes and shout to the others to fasten them round them and jump. But except for the white-duck lunatic, his wife and child, the men on the yacht were sailors, and somehow the miracle—and the awe-struck Island swore later in the day that it was a miracle—was accomplished. A joyous yell from Jacquemin, rising triumphantly above the sound of the waves curling hungrily round those terrible rocks, announced that one more feat of Island daring was accomplished on the sea. Ranulph, strength rushing into him from that shout, raised his head and saw a little drenched half-unconscious morsel of humanity lying across his feet. It was the child from the wreck. For one awful moment, so astray were his wits, he thought it was Colette . . . Then her father—and Ranulph was not too exhausted to notice that he was obviously English and a fool—picked her up, and at Guilbert's shout they bent to their oars again. Ranulph, gripping his oar with hands that seemed now numb and nerveless, wondered if he would get back alive . . . Well, he knew his time to die had come—he'd known it yesterday. The return journey, with the current in their favour, should be easy, but he had not now one drop left of the strength that had brought him out. Yet he went on rowing, pushing the moment of collapse always one stroke further off, and still one stroke further. He heard again the surge of the blood in his ears and then clear above it Guilbert's voice shouting "In the bay!" And suddenly, at that triumphant cry, he came to the end of his surface strength and tapped that supply of hidden power that only the using up of the last drop of surface energy brings into play. Life seemed to flow back again. The ghastly hammering and bursting of his heart and lungs lessened. He drove his oar through the water with a stronger stroke and the crimson curtain lifted from before his eyes. He looked up and saw, with the clearness and yet remoteness of a vision, a vivid magical picture of the Island. In a moment of time he seemed to see it all, down to the tiniest detail. The rain had stopped and patches of fragile blue were showing through rents in the clouds that were now thinning into blown wisps of grey gauze. There was a hint of coming sunlight and the little bay, with the waves flinging white flowery half-moons of creaming foam across its smooth sand, shone brilliantly gold and silver against the sombre cliffs. Up above the purple and indigo of caves and rocky caverns the young spring bracken and hawthorn-trees frothed vividly green between sea and sky, and above them again blue spirals of smoke from pink and white fishermen's cottages streamed away landwards on the wind. For a moment it seemed to Ranulph that the Island, a living presence, slipped between him and this actual scene and showed him all her glories in a moment of time. He saw Bon Repos and the doves dreaming under a hot summer sun, the cobbled streets of St. Pierre and the waters of the harbour lilac under a sunset sky, the round green tunnels of the water-lanes, the market with its fruit and vegetables and curds, the old Church of St. Raphael standing four square to the winds, and the pink rocks and tamarisk-trees of L'Autel. The Island! An Undine spirit of earth and water, a sweet, magical, tempestuous thing that had given him life and would rob him of it. Even as his queer moment of vision passed there was a warning shout from Guilbert.

They were entering the bay and a little careless from exhaustion and victory they had come too close to the rocks that stretched out into the sea from the cliffs at its northern side. A great wave, pouring over the rocks from the heavy sea beyond, hit them just as the calmer waters of the bay had made them relax their vigilance. The boat heeled over, a cold sheet of water drenched and blinded them, and the white-duck Englishman, either from the natural imbecility of his disposition or from shock, let go of the child. She was overboard in an instant and carried swiftly away from the boat by the wash of the wave. Her little wet yellow head seemed to

Ranulph to be Colette's. Before the boat had righted itself he was out of it and after her, so swiftly that with half a dozen strokes he had reached and caught her. But the act was the last of Ranulph's life. Even as he grabbed her the dreaded cramp seized him. Keeping her head above water, and drifting with every moment further from the boat, he fought it and watched with anguish the figure of Guilbert, who had plunged after him and was swimming towards them. Would he be in time? He kept his eyes on Guilbert's arm, curving over his head, cleaving the water with a steady unhurried stroke, curving over his head again, and with his last effort of will pushed the moment of collapse one stroke further off, and still one stroke further off . . . Guilbert reached him . . . "I'm all right," he said, "take the child."

One more moment of sight was his. He could see the sailors struggling to right the swamped boat and get her out of the danger zone, he could see Guilbert, swimming strongly, taking the child towards them, he could see the yellow bay with that flowery crescent of foam thrown across it, and then he deliberately abandoned effort and sank like a stone.

THE WITCH HUNT

UNDER the lowering sky with its dark and phantom clouds the evil of the world seemed crushing him into the earth. There was a cry of terror. He stood still, his breath choking him and his mouth dry. Was it the wind? No, not the wind, or his body would not so echo the fear. It had been a woman's cry, and it had come from his left. Somehow, clutching at the hedge above him with the crook of his stick, he managed to scramble up the bank and push through the bushes. Flying through the dusk of the field he could see dark shadows, the dark forms of men, and they were hunting silently, their silence far more deadly than baying hounds would have been. Their quarry was ahead of them. He could see a gleam of streaming white as of a banner or scarf, but no more, she ran so fast, as fast as a white hare before the hounds.

She was making for the wood that lay beyond the fields, the leafless branches roaring in the wind as though it were a bitter sea that beat upon their dark shore. But she would not find safety there. The men who pursued her were men of the woods and could see in them with the eyes of a cat.

The strength of his youth returned to Parson Hawthyn. The witch hunt was running parallel with the lane and not far from it. He had only a short distance to run before he had come between the woman and her pursuers, and just at that moment she caught her foot in a tuft of grass and fell. By that fall she saved herself, for in a moment Parson Hawthyn had reached her and was standing over her brandishing a stick.

He was a comical knight errant with his sparrow-like figure, crimson face and jutting white beard. He had lost his hat and his priestly white bands were all awry. He was almost as much beside himself with indignation as Froniga had been, but he did not swear, for the depths of him had been purged of their mirk long ago. What welled up from them now was a white-hot flame of anger that was terrifying by reason of its very purity. If the prayer of a righteous man availeth much, so does his anger. It built a wall about the old man and the prostrate woman, and the hunters halted.

"I forbid you to touch this woman," said Parson Hawthyn, brandishing his stick, his voice ringing out powerfully. "And you cannot touch her without killing me first, and I am a rashai. You know what will happen if you kill a rashai; you will yourselves die and your souls will lie for ever in deep hell."

They could tell that he was a rashai by his garments, and a few among them knew him by sight. They had a superstitious fear of parsons. Even to see one was unlucky, to kill one was worse. They drew back a little, as dogs will do when haunted by fear. First one and then another slunk away into the shadows. In a few moments there was no one left but the parson and the witch.

"I think that is all, my daughter," he said. "But you cannot stay alone in your cottage tonight. You must come with me to the village."

He helped her to her feet. He could see that her face was ashen and that she could not control the trembling of her jaw. Her eyes stared towards the glow of fire in the distance and he could imagine what the dread of fire was to a witch. The white thing that he had seen was her apron. It had been torn in her fall and she pulled at it with a sort of fretful anger, as though realizing it had increased her danger. It came away in her hand and she dropped it on the ground.

"I was at the well," she said. "If they had got me in the cottage I could not have escaped." She began to shiver and he took her arm and held it.

"Mistress Skipton," he said sternly, "if you cannot control your trembling I cannot take you to safety. Your will has always been strong for evil, use it now for good. For life is good and you will win life if you will do as I bid you. Come now."

He helped her across the field and they struggled through the hedge together and down the bank into the lane. They stumbled along it, helping each other, for Parson Hawthyn was now once again feeling his rheumatic knees and fatigue. They might both have found progress impossible had it not been for the help of his stick. As they walked he wondered where to take the woman. Though he knew that many of his parishioners secretly made use of her and her spells he did not suppose that any of them would welcome a witch for the night, and he had no room in his own house in which to put her even if she could have walked so far. Then he thought of Froniga. Hers was the first cottage they would reach in the lane, and she was strong and courageous. Moreover he thought in his ignorance that Froniga, being herself half a gypsy, would be in favour with her mother's people and anyone whom she protected would be safe from them.

"Mistress Skipton, I am taking you to Mistress Froniga Haslewood," he said. "Of all of us in the village I think she is best able to protect you."

The witch made no answer. He could not know her state of mind, but guessed she was a creature thrown out of her element and stunned by shock. Her element of evil had been as familiar to her as is its lair to a beast. He wondered if she would be able to make the effort to stay out of it and so to save herself, or whether beast-like she would crawl back to it again.

They came to Froniga's cottage and to his dismay he saw that the windows were dark. If she had gone to spend Christmas at the manor then he did not know what to do, but if she was out attending some sick person then she had probably left her back door unlocked, according to her careless and dangerous custom. They dragged themselves round to the back door, he lifted the latch and to his relief the door opened. In the warm fragrant little room inside a faint glow still came from the fire, and also from the other fire beyond the east window. He put Mother Skipton in Froniga's chair with her back to it and quickly pulled the curtain, threw fresh dry wood and fir-cones on the fire and lit the candles. Then he looked round anxiously. He knew he should give Mother Skipton some hot drink to revive her but he did not know how to come by it.

"Heat me a little hot milk over the fire," said Mother Skipton in a voice faint and dry as the rustle of dead leaves. "She keeps her saucepans there, hanging from those hooks. The milk is in the blue jug on the dresser."

"I see that you've been here before," said Parson Hawthyn, as he did her bidding.

"No," she said, "but I have looked through the window. I have looked through it many times to increase my hatred of her. I have seen her with her witch's hair lying on her shoulders in the arms of her gypsy lover. You have desired to save me from evil. You should look nearer home."

Parson Hawthyn, kneeling on the hearth to warm her milk, steadied himself with his hand against the wall. He looked at her. The words had been venomous, but her eyes were blank and unseeing. If the venom had been in her eyes too he would have given up all hope for her. As it was he felt wretched enough. He had heard of the taming of wild beasts, but he had never heard of a tame adder. He gave the woman the cup of hot milk and turned to warm his hands at the fire, trying not to see that picture of Froniga that her words had conjured up in his mind. Presently they drew up their chairs to the fire and sat in silence. Mother Skipton, when she had finished her milk, sat with her eyes shut and without movement. The old man tried to pray, but he was too tired and confused, and before his eyes if he closed them was always that picture of Froniga.

There was a quick step outside, the latch lifted and there she was. She saw Mother Skipton and joy and relief banished the white weariness from her face. Her cheeks and her eyes flowed with the joy, and the generosity of it wiped the other image of her out of Parson Hawthyn's mind and he never thought of it again.

Froniga went to Mother Skipton and put her hand on her shoulder. "Thank heaven you are safe," she said, and then turned to Parson Hawthyn. "Did you find her?"

"Yes," he said, reaching for his stick and getting to his feet. "She has been in great danger from the Romany people, but she has escaped by the mercy of God. Look after her, Froniga, I must go home." He limped to the door and she went with him in concern, for she did not think he looked able to walk home. "Stay here and rest a little longer," she begged.

He drew her outside the door and closed it. "Your concern is not with me, but with that poor woman," he said. "Keep her with you now, and after Christmas we will consult together on her behalf. I put a heavy burden on you, but you are strong. Do not let her go back to her cottage. If she did so it would be like —"

"A dog returning to its vomit," interrupted Froniga. "I know. I've been there. I'll do my best. Have you lost something?"

"I had a bunch of flowers and leaves," he said sadly. "They gave it to me in Henley for the church. Well, of course, I dropped it. I cannot go back."

"There are even now many fair things in my garden," said Froniga warmly. "I'll bring all I can find to the church in the morning."

"I will be glad of them. Good-night, Froniga."

BLIND AUTHOR

PAUL, at work at this hour in his small study with Bess asleep on the floor beside him, needed no candles. It gave Valerie the horrors, when presently she looked in to say she was going up to bed, to see him sitting in the dark. "It's so morbid," she said. "Why can't you put the light on just for the look of the thing?"

"Why waste electricity just for the look of the thing?"

"You waste so many things, why not electricity?"

"What do I waste?"

"Your time for one thing. When you're in here half the time you're not using your typewriter at all, or your tape-recorder, you're simply sitting doing nothing." He smiled, his slow amused smile that so maddened her, as though he had a private joke with himself from which she was shut out. "And you call that work; I believe you think you're earning our living. Don't stay up late. When you come up so late, and wake me just when I've got off, I can't sleep again for hours. You know I can't."

"I'll be quiet, Val."

"You never are. You knock into things. Why can't you work in the morning when other men do?"

"Because I'm no good in the morning. And there's no peace in this house in the morning." He broke off, for it was fast developing into one of their altercations. "I'm sorry, darling, but it has to be this way. One day, when I've written my best seller, I'll make it all up to you."

He was smiling at her but she wouldn't look at him. While they had argued she had switched the light on. Now she went away deliberately leaving it burning. It gave her a secret pleasure to think that he thought he was in the dark and he wasn't.

Paul sat for a few moments hunched forward in his chair, his hands locked together between his knees. It was almost the attitude of physical pain. Bess stirred in her sleep, turned and laid her chin on his feet. Valerie had been an enchanting and pretty girl. He was perfectly well aware of the change in her. Whenever he tried to visualize her the thin hard face slipped like a mask over the face that he remembered, and wanted to remember, and repulsed him as she herself repulsed him whenever he tried to restore again some measure of the love that had once been between them. Yet he believed that it was still only a mask, not the reality as yet. If he could only get through he would find his girl alive behind it. Would it have been all right if he had not been blinded, or if he had done what she had wanted and let himself be trained in one of the skills that blind men could practise so lucratively? But he had always wanted to write, and tried to write, even in his sighted days, and after he had been blinded he had wanted it with an obstinate intensity that had swept away every objection laid before him by his parents and sensible friends, and even the pleadings of Valerie herself. He had had to do this thing, come what might, though as a naturally confident and hopeful person he had believed in himself and expected to succeed. He had never imagined that after years of hard work he would still be earning so little. Yet it made no difference. He wrote because he had to and for no other reason. It did not even occur to him to give it up for Valerie's sake and even at this late date get himself trained for something else. Nor had he considered living in the town, as Valerie wanted, or going to bed at a reasonable hour. He always felt ill and without the quiet of the country and the night he would not have been able to write. There was possibly a streak of selfishness in his single-mindedness but though he did not much care whether he succeeded or not he still half-believed that he would. He had a small but growing reputation as a poet, a prestige reputation of which Valerie knew nothing but which he hugged to himself with secret joy, a couple of plays were even now hovering near to production and there was the book.

It was the book which it is said every man can write, that semi-autobiographical book which is as much a record of a man's spirit as of his life, and which he fondly imagines to be fiction from beginning to end. Paul, playwright and poet, had never even contemplated writing a novel until three months ago. A difficult poem finished at last, he had been in the usual restless, nervy, miserable condition. He had been longing to get to the end of it yet without it he had felt intolerably bereaved. And he had known he would never write another line, and told himself that he never wanted to. Writing was an exhausting senseless business, a mug's game. Yet all the while he had been feeling frantically around in his dusty mind for ideas, like a miser who has dropped his gold in the dark, with desolation growing in him all the time like a bottomless pit. He should have recognized the symptoms as the first pangs of a new poem, for they followed each other regularly in the same order whenever he was not working, but he never did recognize them.

And then suddenly in the middle of the night it had happened again, and it had been new as spring, though it had happened so many times. It had not this time been a line of verse crying out like a lost spirit for habitation, giving him no rest until word by word and sound by sound he had built up the form it wanted. Nor had it been as when a play was beginning and a vivid scene flashed before his inward eyes, men in movement, in conflict, in some dilemma from which he must rescue them or neither he nor they would know rest again. This had been a presence with him, a quiet man standing at the end of his bed. He had seen him clearly, and seen too the foot of the bed that he had never seen. The man had been dark, physically unlike himself, his fine head and strong shoulders as magnificently sculptured as those of a statue. He had been suffering but dumb; like the Polish officer who had once occupied the bed in a hospital ward next to Paul and whose anguish had been locked within himself because those about him did not know a word of his language. He had seemed to Paul to represent all the men who suffered in war and, if they lived, came home again as speechless as they had gone out. Or if they tried to speak they found the common language had no adequate words; and so their sons must suffer all over again. "I'll try," he had said to the man. "I'll say it for you." But the man's suffering had been in no way relieved and would not be relieved until the book was finished.

And it seemed to Paul, sitting slumped in his chair, that it never would be finished. He was only a third of the way through and already he was played out. And the thing would not come alive. It lacked the vital fire. Yet he had to go on for the man's sake. What

243

lunatics writers are, he thought. He was madder even than dear old Miss Lindsay. Get on, you fool, he said to himself. He sat back in his chair, and Bess lifted her chin from his feet and went comfortably to sleep again. He relaxed, trying to loosen the hold of every thought that still held him to time or place, to integrate himself for the effort of concentration that would set the spring within flowing. At first he had found it appallingly difficult to write like this, entirely within his mind. In his sighted days he had thought with his pen in his hand, writing a few words, then pausing to think again, able to look back at will, checking what he had written with what he was thinking. To create a whole chapter or scene in his mind, remembering and co-ordinating it without recourse to pen and paper, had seemed at first impossible, but now that he had learnt the art of withdrawal within himself he found it a more satisfying way of writing than the other because giving more consciously from the depths of himself he could feel that he had given all he had to give. But it was more exhausting, and it called for deeper concentration and quiet. As to results, he tried not to worry. He would have liked to have been in the first class but that was beyond one's control. If one's intellectual equipment was not great, one's spiritual experience not deep, the result of doing one's damned best could only seem very lightweight in comparison with the effort involved. But perhaps that was not important. The mysterious power that commanded men appeared to him to ask of them only obedience and the maximum of effort and to remain curiously indifferent as to results. For an hour he sat motionless, outwardly as relaxed as though he slept, inwardly at full stretch. Then he pulled the small table that held his tape-recorder towards him, picked up the microphone and dictated straight through without pause. Then he repeated the process and the clock struck twelve.

He had finished work for the night but he sat on listening to the sounds of the night that he loved more than those of the day. Intensely sensitive to the music of sound as he had become, the crashing symphony of the day sometimes almost overwhelmed him; especially in the spring when the birds and the children had gone mad, when the spring rains rushed upon the new leaves and Valerie started her spring-cleaning. But the night music was quiet as one of Beethoven's gentler sonatas, the notes falling with grave precision. There was the tick of his clock, the creak of the tired old stair treads as they relaxed in the dark, the rustle of a mouse, an owl calling and the slow deep breathing of Bess. And other infinitesimal sounds that he had never heard when he was sighted, the eddying of air on a windless night, the tinkle of dew, the breathing of trees and the steps of the moonlight. It might be that he imagined these sounds. He did not know. But if he did they were none the less exquisite for that.

It was time for bed and he moved in his chair. Bess was instantly awake and standing by him, her silken tail swishing expectantly. Every new activity, though it was merely a repetition of daily routine, was hailed by Bess as a thrilling occurrence. To eat, to sleep, to wake, to go upstairs or downstairs, to go for a walk, to come home, it was all equally wonderful to Bess because it was Paul's world that controlled these things and she trembled to his will as a compass needle to the north. She was trembling now with eagerness to be put out, not for any need of nature because Valerie had already put her out, but because he wanted to put her out. They went together to the study door and Paul turned off the light. He had heard Valerie switch it on and knew why she had not turned it off. These small cruelties now hurt him less than they did. His love for her was tired he supposed. She made it difficult for him to love her.

Bess took him to the back door and was let out, and he stood leaning in the doorway while she chased her tail in the moonlight. Beyond the tiny kitchen garden he was aware of the orchard and the glory of motionless blossom. There was that apple-tree there, just over the fence. Fallen and broken it still lived and bore fruit. Suddenly parting from routine, to the astonishment of Bess, he left the door and walked down the short grass path to the low fence. Here he only had to stretch out a hand and he could feel the blossoms of the fallen tree. They were cool and wet with dew and in his mind's eye he could see their pale glimmer under the moon. There were so many of them. This fallen tree bore fruit as richly as any in the orchard, a round red little apple, crisp when one bit into it and very fresh. The dew was heavy tonight, and most welcome in this dry spell. As always after working too hard his scarred face felt tight and hot, but the coolness of the dew and its faint scent eased him. The scent of water, of the rain and of the dew. It was difficult to separate it from the grateful fragrance of the life it renewed, but it had its scent; the faint exhalation of its goodness. It would still come down upon the earth after man, destroying himself, had destroyed also the leaves and the grass. Its goodness might even renew again the face of the burnt and blasted earth. He did not know. But unlike Job's comforters he believed there was a supreme goodness that could renew his own soul beyond this wasting sorrow of human life and death.

Bess pressed against his knee. He fondled her head and it was wet with dew. They went back to the cottage and crept stealthily upstairs, terrified lest a stair creak and wake Valerie. Paul no longer slept with his wife. Valerie had her wide bed and charming south room to herself and Paul had the small room over his study. When he and Bess had got inside, and he had managed to shut the door without its creaking, he sighed with relief. With any luck he'd get to bed soundlessly. But his luck was out, for Valerie had left a tin of furniture polish on the floor and he trod on it and stumbled against the wall. He listened anxiously and heard the creak of her bed as she turned over, her cough and loud weary sigh. She never let him remain in ignorance of the fact that he had wakened her. He crept into bed and lay awake until a sudden burst of joyous music bubbled up from the throat of a small bird beneath his window. He could not see the first ray of light to which the bird responded but its song was all the more wonderful to him because he couldn't. Comforted, he turned over and slept.

NIGHT RESCUE

THE next day, Saturday, November 24th, the wind changed and freshened as Tom Pearse had foretold. Clouds had come up before the wind and it was quite dark when the doctor got back from his rounds, and he and Zachary sat down rather late to their evening meal. The Admiral had signalled an immediate departure just before five o'clock, Tom Pearse told them as he handed the vegetables. They did not ask how he knew this. He always knew everything. News travelled among the country people with quite miraculous rapidity, and if it was anything to do with the fleet Tom Pearse seemed to be able to smell it in the mind of a man a mile off.

"It'll be a job to work out of the bay in this darkness, sir," he said to the doctor. "Dirty weather on the way too. Better to have waited till morning."

The doctor looked at the opaque blackness outside the window, and in the little pause they could hear the moan of the rising wind.

"Admiral Cornwallis knows his job," he said slowly.

Tom Pearse sniffed dubiously and poured out the claret.

The doctor and Zachary were sitting reading in front of the study fire when they heard the low boom of a gun. The doctor lifted his head and waited. Ship in distress. Tom Pearse's head came round the door. "Puttin' in Aesculapius, sir," he said briefly. The doctor grunted, read steadily to the end of the paragraph, then closed his book and reached for his doctor's bag. "Coming, Zachary?" he asked. Zachary nodded and got up.

Bundled up in thick coats the three of them packed into the gig and drove off into the windy darkness. Scuds of rain came now and then upon the wind, lashing their faces. The darkness hindered their pace not at all, for Aesculapius knew every inch of these roads. Yet he slowed down as they neared Smokyhouse, where the door stood open showing the glow of firelight, and a man's bulky figure blocked against it. He hailed them and the doctor stopped. "Take me along with 'ee, doctor?" shouted George Spratt. "Make haste then, George," the doctor called back. George swung himself up behind, breathing beer down their necks, and they were off again, swaying perilously down the steep hill, the roar of the sea sounding always louder in their ears.

"The *Venerable*, Captain Hunter, on the rocks at Paignton Ledge," growled George. "Allus the one ship lost in every great storm. Torbay claims her."

Zachary pondered this idea of George Spratt's, remembering the doctor's story of the day before. Was there some sort of demon in Torbay, living down there in the submerged forest, that yielded the antlers of deer to the fishermen's nets, that now and again must claim a victim?

"Know any details, George?" asked the doctor.

George knew all about it, of course. While the *Venerable*'s anchor was being secured one of the seamen had fallen from it. A boat was ordered away but one of the falls being let go too soon it was swamped, a midshipman and two sailors being drowned . . . Zachary felt cold, thinking of that wretched midshipman . . . A second boat was lowered and the first sailor saved. Meanwhile all the ships were tacking, but the *Venerable* having lost way was unable to gain her position, and to avoid collision was forced close to the shore. The heavy swell had caught her and now she was on the rocks on Paignton Ledge. It was George's opinion that the guns would not avail her much, for the rest of the fleet was probably out of hearing.

Paignton village was deserted, for everyone had gone down to the shore. They put up Aesculapius and the gig at the inn, where one lame ostler had been left in charge, and fought their way down to the beach through the wind and rain. The flares and hurricane lamps lit up a scene that seemed to Zachary like some scene in hell. The crowd upon the beach might have been a multitude of lost souls, figures and faces now hidden in darkness, now leaping suddenly into view lit by crimson light. The waves breaking on the beach leaped savagely, the flung white spray turned to flecks of fire now and then by the flares, and the scream of the wind rising above the boom of the guns was a dreadful thing to hear.

They could dimly make out the doomed ship on the rocks. The sea had made a complete breach in her and the waves were pouring through. At sight of her, and at thought of the men aboard her, all his old hatred of the sea swept over Zachary, sickening him. Then the nausea passed and rage took its place. Why was no one doing anything? Were they all to stand here and watch those men drown? He must have shouted aloud in his fury for he felt the doctor take his arm and shake it, shouting something unintelligible. Then he saw that there were some boats tossing about the *Venerable*, and that a handful of courageous fishermen were trying to get more boats off from the beach. Evidently the guns had been heard by at least two of the other ships, they had sent their boats, and the order had now been given to abandon ship. The *Venerable* was almost on her beam ends now and looked as though she might break in two at any moment. Yet her guns still fired, and would do as long as any of her seamen remained on board.

Then began one of the most splendid efforts to save life that Torbay had ever witnessed. The fight continued all through that stormy pitch-black night. One after the other, the small pitching boats passed under the *Venerable*'s stern, and her officers, keeping the saving of their own lives till the last, helped their men in. Lines were flung and made fast on the shore, and other men tried to haul themselves along to safety, but the surf was so tremendous that most of those making the attempt were either drowned or dashed to pieces upon the rocks. There was less loss of life from the boats, for few of these attempted to get to shore but rowed out to sea to the ships that had sent them, but some were capsized, and no one could survive in that terrible sea. At five in the morning Captain Hunter at last consented to leave his ship. In single file, the junior officer leading, the officers and ten seamen who had declared they would die with their officers and refused to leave without them, scrambled into the last two boats, while a few officers, for whom there was no room in the boats, succeeded in climbing to safety along the bowsprit. Only one man was left behind, a drunken marine who refused to get into the last boat. He alone went down with the *Venerable*.

Throughout that night Zachary worked as hard and as courageously as any man upon the beach. Soon after the doctor had shaken him by the arm he found himself in one of the boats, taking an oar behind George Spratt. Theirs was one of the few boats that got out to the *Venerable* and back with a boatload of sailors without capsizing. Later he was in the sea, up to the waist in ice-cold water, Tom Pearse beside him, struggling to save the exhausted men clinging to the lines. Later still he was inside the inn at the harbour, labouring with the doctor to bring back life to half-drowned bodies. And all through the night it was his rage that kept him going, rage lit now and then by some sort of light, a triumph of some kind. He reasoned nothing out through the turmoil of the night; just found himself possessed alternately by the rage and triumph.

It was still dark when at last there was no more for them to do; and the rescuers carried the rescued back to their homes with them, for hot drinks, hot baths and bed. The doctor captured two young officers and drove them home in the gig. Zachary, George Spratt and Tom Pearse followed on foot. They were too weary for much speech, but Tom said to Zachary, "You did a man's work this night, sir," and George growled agreement. Zachary nodded. He knew he had. His rage had gone now, but the triumph remained, and though his teeth were chattering it warmed him through.

STELLA'S PUNISHMENT

A JERK of Sol's thumb upward checked him. Stella was leaning out of her window and calling, "I did it, Father! I did it!" "Eh?" ejaculated Father Sprigg, red-faced, perspiring, almost throttling himself as he choked upon his wrath. "*You* left the door abroad, poppet?"

"Yes," said Stella. "It wasn't Sol, it was me. I took the bar down and then I couldn't get it up again. I took the pigeon pie too, and milk from the dairy, and gave them to that ragged boy."

Both men gaped up at her in astonishment and Father Sprigg took out his handkerchief and mopped his forehead.

"I'm strong," explained Stella. "Hodge helped."

Hodge was standing up on his hind legs beside her now, his furry face framed beside hers in the little window. Father Sprigg blew out his cheeks, exhaled the air in a long whistling breath of bewilderment, turned and brought a hand like a large ham penitently down on Sol's shoulder. If he was quick to wrath he was equally quick in making amends if he found himself mistaken. "A little maid like her!" he ejaculated with admiration as Stella withdrew from the window to get dressed.

But his admiration had evaporated by the time they met again at breakfast and his anger was smouldering once more. If Stella ever did such a thing again he'd turn her upside down and spank her, big girl though she was, he declared between mighty mouthfuls of porridge, and it was no idle threat either, he meant what he said. Had she not those damned stable cats to pamper, and that vinny bag of bones, Daniel, a fool not worth his keep and kept only to pleasure her, but she must go wasting good vittles on some dirty scoundrel who might have murdered them all in their beds? He paused to stick a hunk of bread into his mouth and Mother Sprigg carried on where he left off. Stella had never seen her so annoyed. Had she not told Stella time and again that she must never speak to strangers, especially disreputable strangers? She might have come to some terrible harm and if she had it would have been entirely her own fault, and a just punishment for as flagrant an act of disobedience as Mother Sprigg had ever heard of in all her days. Here Madge and old Sol murmured agreement and shook their heads sadly. Seraphine, presiding over her kittens beside the fire, had her back turned to Stella. Only Hodge, sitting beside her chair and pressing his head hard against her knee, was on her side.

But Stella went on placidly eating her porridge and was not disturbed. She knew perfectly well that all this disapproval was caused by nothing but love. If there had been no danger to her in what she had done they would not have been so angry. But she did not say she was sorry because she was not. She knew she had done perfectly right to feed Zachary Moon. She knew that the inside people must always help the outside people. But she was sorry that she could not say she was sorry because she could see that her silence was exasperating Father and Mother Sprigg worse than ever.

"She shan't be spanked this time, Father, since you say not," said Mother Sprigg, "but punished she must be. It's her morning for going to the doctor for her lessons. She must bide at home; both to punish her and to keep her safe from that scoundrel, if he's still about."

Stella looked up quickly, dropping her spoon, wounded to the quick. Her lessons with Dr. Crane were the most precious hours in her week, and Mother Sprigg knew it. The face she turned to her foster mother was white and set hard. Mother Sprigg was jealous of her lessons, afraid of them for some reason, and now she was using this necessity for punishment as an opportunity to stop Stella learning things. It was not fair. The little girl got up, went to the cupboard under the window-seat where she kept her treasures and came back with the ruler that Dr. Crane had given her.

"Father," she said, standing in front of him, "please, I do not want to give up my lessons. If Mother does not wish me to be out in the lanes by myself Sol will come with me to the village; you said yesterday he must take Bess to the blacksmith. And Dr. Crane will bring me back in his gig before he starts his rounds. Please, Father, instead of keeping me in will you whip me instead. Please will you whip me just as hard as ever you can." She laid the ruler beside his plate and held out her slim beautiful little hands, considering them. "My left hand, please, Father, because I shall want to hold my pen in my right." She put her right hand behind her, out of harm's way, and held out her left. "Hard, please, Father."

Though it was an age when corporal punishment for the young was highly esteemed he had never whipped her yet; he loved her far too well. But now, meeting her unflinching look with one of deep respect, he picked up the ruler, swung round in his chair and gave it to her good and hard until her little palm was scarlet, and the ruler, not designed for corporal punishment, broke in his hand. Then he flung it into a corner, swore, and rising left the room as near tears as Mother Sprigg had ever seen him.

THE DEATH LEAP

HE had expected to be put against a tree trunk and shot and it was a surprise to find himself being dragged up a steep rocky path that wound up the cliff face. To the cat-footed Maoris the climb was easy but the lame Samuel found it arduous. "Free my hands," he said to Tiki. "I can climb more easily then. I shall not try to escape."

There was a howl of protest from the other Maoris when Tiki

did so, but he shot venomous words at them over his shoulder and they did not protest again.

In halting, breathless sentences Samuel tried to talk to Tiki as they climbed. "I did not kill Taketu, Tiki," he said.

"Then whom do you accuse?" asked Tiki savagely.

"I accuse no one," said Samuel gently. "But I tell you again it was not I who killed Taketu. The God whom I serve is not a destroyer of life, like your Tu, but the preserver of it, and His servants do not kill. My God is Creator, Saviour, Comforter and Strengthener. He made men, He loves them, He died for them, He saves those who believe on Him from the power of evil, from the devils, from sin and disease. He comforts them in sorrow and makes them so strong in death that they cannot be held by its bands and pass with gladness into the world beyond." He stopped, breathless, doubtful if Tiki had listened to a word, yet driven to go on by the fact that what he had wanted, that last chance to speak again, had been given to him, even if his audience was only this one inattentive boy. "Our heaven is not as your Reinga," he went on, "a land of exile and loneliness where your gods give you no comfort. We go there not weeping but rejoicing because we shall there be in the presence of a God so glorious that the torture and death of the body are a small price to pay that we may see His face and serve Him for ever in the spirit land."

"Mighty words," said Tiki contemptuously. "Mighty like the wind. And I know that only Tuas show no fear when they die. Men of peace show fear. For all your wind of words you will be afraid."

"Because I die for the God who died for me I shall not be afraid," said Samuel. "Because of my death you will ask yourself, 'Who is this God that men should die thus for Him?' And you will remember what I taught you about my God, and you will seek out other men who will teach you more. You Maoris do not die for the honour of your gods, Tiki, because your gods have never died for you. Death tests love, and the love that stands the test is the greatest treasure in the world. With such a love does my God love me, and I possess His love, and with such a love do I love Him."

Tiki grunted and Samuel's halting sentences failed him altogether, for they had entered the steep gully in the rock that led

253

directly up to the Torere, and he had no breath. He was not altogether sorry, for what was the use of saying anything when his words were so paltry and his hearer so inattentive? Tiki moved behind him, for they could climb now only in single file. The moon had risen and it was almost as bright as daylight. Some half-dozen of the Maoris were climbing in front of Samuel and the rest were behind Tiki. His world narrowed to the chimney of rock where he was and all his energy and thought were concentrated on the effort to get up it.

They reached the ledge of rock before the entrance to the cave and instantly the Maoris began to wail and lament. Samuel guessed that this was the Torere and that the bodies of Te Turi and Taketu were now within it. The Maoris shunned the Toreres, he knew, and he was not surprised when a gust of superstitious fear carried them all past it as though they were a handful of bronzed autumn leaves before the wind. Then they were climbing again, up the sheer rock face this time, and Samuel was terrified lest he should not be able to get up it, and his physical failure be mistaken by Tiki for the terror shown in the face of death by men of peace. Tiki's eyes scarcely ever left him now, he knew. He could feel the boy's whole consciousness focused upon him as though he were some midge of a creature pinned down beneath the microscope. And not only Tiki's consciousness. The boy's eyes were like a focal point of vision that widened out into a blaze of light that enveloped the whole of existence. All that ever was, that ever would be, watched through Tiki's eyes. He knew then, if he had not known before, the ultimate importance of one human soul.

Just when he thought he was beaten, that he could drag himself up the rock not one inch further, his physical ordeal ended and he stumbled out into what seemed to him, in his dazed condition, the ante-room of heaven. Had he died already? Had he died climbing the rock? No. The pain of wrenched limbs and panting breath told him that he was still in this world, but that mother earth, whose beauty he had delayed to acknowledge and worship almost until his last breath, was being merciful to him. She was too great-hearted to withhold the full reward even from those who came only to the vineyard in the cool of the day.

He was standing in the full moonlight in the centre of that small and beautiful amphitheatre in the rocky hillside where Hine-Moa had made a resting place for her white folk. Now, as then, it was carpeted with grass and flowers, and wind-tossed mountain larches bent over from the forest of them that climbed the hillside above, but now the brightness of bright moons gave to its beauty an unearthliness that hushed even the Maoris to a motionless silence. Each flower petal was like a sea shell of mother-of-pearl, each veined leaf a tiny sword of silver. The larch trunks were polished ivory beneath the weightless cloud-like canopies of shimmering leaves that they lifted up and up, higher and higher on the hillside, until at last the brightness of them was lost in the brightness of moonlit snow. That mountain that Samuel loved seemed very close now, towering up into the sky with the stars motionless about its head. He looked his last at it, then turned and looked out over the forest far down at the foot of the precipice that they had lately climbed, so far away that it was like a silvery shroud spread upon the floor of the world. Down there beneath it birds nested and animals had their lairs, men hunted, women built hearthfires and little children played. But for him these familiar things were past and over, muffled away beneath a shroud. The stillness was like ice, benumbing him, and there came to him suddenly the feeling that everything was slipping away. Nothing moved and yet everything was leaving him. He was on the brink of an awful darkness, the kind that children dread, that unknown darkness that is on the other side of a drawn curtain in a lighted room. He would be in it soon, with everything familiar left behind on the wrong side of the curtain. All in a moment his adoration of earth's beauty was lost in a sickening fear, the last fear of all, and the worst.

Then that too passed and he knew that between the moment when he had staggered out into this lovely place, and the moment that the icy fear let go of him, had ticked away not an hour but only a minute of clock time. It had seemed a lifetime but it had only been sixty seconds. He straightened himself and looked round at the Maoris, smiling. They were closing in upon him, very watchful. He was vaguely aware of the Tohunga, not quite satisfied with the turn that things were taking, and vividly aware of Tiki, whose eyes were never off him for a moment. He knew why the Tohunga was not satisfied . . . He had not failed yet . . . He had shown no fear when things went against him at the séance, he had managed to climb up the precipice without assistance, though it had been a hard test of endurance for a man weakened by the long strain of the night's uncertainty, he could smile as they closed in upon him. But the thoughts of the Tohunga were nothing to him. It was Tiki who mattered.

At a signal from the Tohunga two of the Maoris sprang, lithe as panthers, and dragged him towards the edge of the precipice. He knew now what they were going to do with him. They were going to hurl him over. Tiki had chosen for him a merciful death, as deaths go, yet from the Maori point of view full of poetic justice, for as he hurtled down his body would fall past the opening of the cave where Taketu lay buried.

"Let go!" he cried to the men who were dragging him forward. "You need not throw me over like an animal. For the glory of my God I'll jump without your help."

"Let go of him," commanded Tiki. "Let's see if he will do it."

They let go of him and he swung round to face them, though of the many eyes that watched him he was conscious only of Tiki's.

"The Maori people have given me hospitality, for which I thank them," he said. "And to you, Tiki, I owe my thanks for mercy in my death. You are tino tangata and I will not forget you."

Then with the eagerness of a young man going to his bridal, of a hunter on the trail or a Tua speeding to his first fight, commending his soul to God and his body to the keeping of the earth, he ran and leaped and fell.

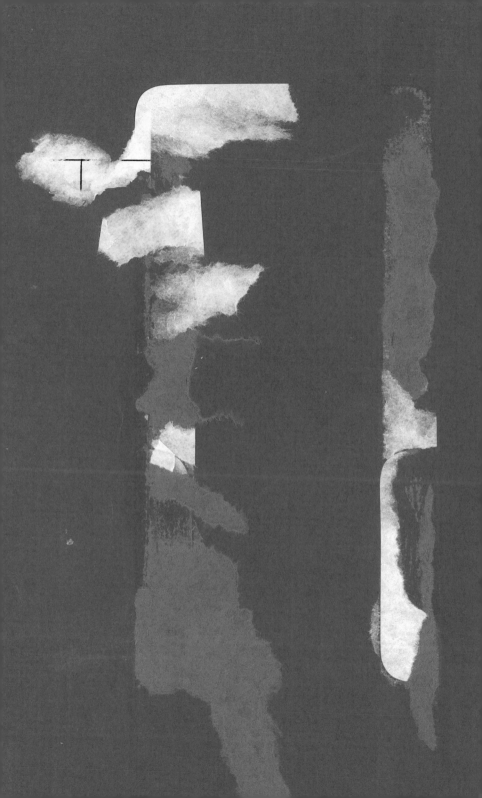